JOHN IRELAND

THE
COLLECTED PIANO WORKS

Volume 2

Stainer & Bell Limited acknowledge the ready co-operation of copyright holders in allowing works to be used in this collected edition and thank the John Ireland Trust for a generous contribution towards the cost of publication.

Foreword © 1976 Stainer & Bell Ltd
ISBN 0-85249-394-0

STAINER & BELL

FOREWORD

Ever since the closing years of the eighteenth century, when Clementi, Dussek and J. B. Cramer settled here, London has been a major European centre for the composition and performance of piano music. John Field, Irish composer of the first piano nocturnes, was a pupil of Clementi; Field's contemporary, G. F. Pinto, wrote seven piano sonatas before his tragically early death at the age of nineteen. Their successor, Sterndale Bennett, the most important of the early English Romantics, gained international recognition while still a student at the Royal Academy, then in Tenterden Street. (Schumann, who was deeply impressed by Bennett's concertos and shorter piano pieces, described him as "a pianist above all things".) And it was in London that John Ireland, the greatest writer of piano music among our later Romantic composers, spent virtually the whole of his working life.

Ireland (1879-1962) studied composition at the Royal College under "that great man" Stanford. At the age of 17 he was appointed assistant organist at Holy Trinity, Sloane Street; in 1904 he moved to Chelsea, where he lived for nearly fifty years. Besides playing the organ at St Luke's Parish Church (from 1904 to 1926), John Ireland taught composition at the R.C.M. Among his pupils were many of the outstanding writers of the next generation, most notably Benjamin Britten.

Ireland had a great feeling for places and people, so it is not surprising that London and Londoners figure frequently in his music. He also loved the Channel Islands (*The Island Spell; Sarnia*) and Sussex (*Equinox; Amberley Wild Brooks*); in fact he spent his last years in a converted windmill facing Chanctonbury Ring on the Sussex Downs. Another major influence was the writings of Arthur Machen (*The Scarlet Ceremonies; Legend* for piano and orchestra). He also had a close affinity with A. E. Housman and Thomas Hardy, and his settings of their poetry are among the masterpieces of English song.

On one occasion Ireland repudiated the suggestion that he was a great composer, but added that he was "a significant one". This is a characteristic understatement. Ireland's piano music is as vital a contribution to the British tradition as is that of Fauré to the French; and the work of both composers (wholly personal, yet at the same time completely characteristic of their own countries) is an enrichment of the heritage of European music.

He had decided views about the performance of his own work. One interpreter, who studied over the years with the composer, has written: "Ireland's own playing had an intensity and finish that he expected in others. He was most particular about melodic lines, and would often mark copies with the pencilled words *firm, emphatic*, or *significant*. Tempo was always an important consideration; any sense of hurry was to be avoided. Whether the harmonic scheme was rich or astringent, chord changes had to be clearly heard, and rhythms had to be incisive."

The items in this collected edition are arranged in chronological order, with the exception of the Piano Sonata which is published by itself as Volume Five. Such errors in previous editions as have come to light have been corrected, with the assistance of Eric Parkin and Alan Rowlands. The complete solo piano works have been recorded by Alan Rowlands on Lyrita RCS 15, 23, 24, 28 and 29 (mono); the principal works by Eric Parkin on Lyrita SRCS 87, 88 and 89 (stereo).

GEOFFREY BUSH

January, 1976.   *Music Adviser, The John Ireland Trust*

THE COLLECTED PIANO WORKS OF JOHN IRELAND

ACKNOWLEDGMENTS

Merry Andrew and *Summer Evening* are printed and engraved plates used by kind permission of Chappell & Co. Ltd.

The remaining works are controlled by Stainer & Bell Ltd.

CHELSEA REACH

John Ireland

Tempo di Barcarole (♩.= 40–44)

Published by Stainer & Bell Ltd, 82 High Road, London N2 9PW

Chelsea: Autumn, 1917.

RAGAMUFFIN

Con moto, ma non troppo allegro (♩= 100 - 108)

John Ireland

PIANO

Chelsea: Autumn. 1917

SOHO FORENOONS

John Ireland

BY THE MERE

JOHN IRELAND

IN THE MEADOW

JOHN IRELAND

THE HUNT'S UP

JOHN IRELAND

To William Murdoch

MERRY-ANDREW

JOHN IRELAND

THE TOWING-PATH

John Ireland

SUMMER EVENING

Andantino ♩=69 – 72
in flexible time

JOHN IRELAND

PIANO

42

col Ped.

Chelsea:1913

THE DARKENED VALLEY

Walking along the darkened valley
With silent Melancholy.

Blake

Allegretto sostenuto (♩ = 63–66)

John Ireland

FOR REMEMBRANCE

John Ireland

Andantino con moto (♩ = 56 = 63)

PIANO

50

July 1921.

AMBERLEY WILD BROOKS

John Ireland

Con moto moderato, quasi allegro comodo (♩= 96–104)

Come prima ma più tranquillo

pp dolciss.
una corda

p

pp lontano

Ped.

poco tenuto

ppp leggiero

Ped. al fine

loco

June 1921

EQUINOX

John Ireland

Poco agitato ($\quad$ = 108–112)

PIANO

mf

col Ped.

Autumn, 1922.

Pro amicitia

ON A BIRTHDAY MORNING

John Ireland

Allegro poco vivace ($\quarternote$ = 104-108)

PIANO

mf (gaily)

cresc.

f

mp

mp

p

(rit. un pochiss.)

64

Tempo I

68

February 22, 1922

SOLILOQUY

John Ireland

March, 1922

Printed in Great Britain by Galliard (Printers) Ltd Great Yarmouth

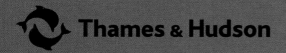
Thames & Hudson

PERFORMANCE NOW

RoseLee Goldberg

With over 260 illustrations

First published in the United Kingdom in 2018 by
Thames & Hudson Ltd, 181a High Holborn, London WC1V 7QX

Performance Now © 2018 Thames & Hudson Ltd.

Text © 2018 RoseLee Goldberg

British Library Cataloguing-in-Publication Data
A catalogue record for this book is available from
the British Library

ISBN 978-0-500-02125-5

Printed in China by Shanghai Offset Printing Products Limited

To find out about all our publications, please visit
www.thamesandhudson.com. There you can subscribe
to our e-newsletter, browse or download our current catalogue,
and buy any titles that are in print.

ON THE COVER Robin Rhode, *Apparatus*, 2009.
C-prints mounted on Plexiglass. 36 parts, each:
35.6 x 53.3cm (14 x 21 in.).

PAGE 1 Araya Rasdjarmrearnsook, *Two Planets: Millet's
The Gleaners and Thai Farmers*, 2008. Film still. Thailand.

PAGE 2-3 Nicholas Hlobo, *Ungamqhawuli*, 2008.
Michael Stevenson Gallery, Cape Town.

THIS PAGE Pussy Riot Punk Prayer, *2012*.
Red Square, Moscow.

CONTENTS

INTRODUCTION

Performance Now charts the development of live visual art across six continents in the years since the new millennium. It shows how performance, so integral to the history of art in the 20th century but largely ignored by art museums and academia, has, in the opening years of the 21st century, become one of the most highly visible art forms in museums as well as at biennials and art fairs around the globe. Newly established performance art departments in contemporary museums, with specialist curators and archivists, are actively developing performance collections, dedicated performance spaces are under construction and art history and performance studies departments are now accepting graduate and postgraduate dissertations that fill the gaps where performance was previously left out, writing a revisionist art history of the last hundred years.

Indeed, performance art is now being inserted into the timeline of a broad range of cultural studies, including theatre and dance history, film, video and architecture, with equal parts theory and analysis. These new areas of study are shifting understandings of 'the live' as a significant visual art form, emphasizing, among other facets: the ways in which performance allows for the layering of ideas and commentary, to reflect the multi-tasking ethos of our times; how it incorporates fast-paced new technologies that are available to most; and its potential for reaching ever broader audiences as a result of the interactive engagement and communal viewing experience that are in this work's very nature.

DIDIER FAUSTINO
Hand Architecture, *2009.*
LAXArt, Los Angeles.

Performance and live events have become part of the regular offerings of major historic museums – the Louvre, the Metropolitan Museum, the British Museum – all of which recognize the increasing interest of viewers in approaching their collections from a lively contemporary perspective. These events combine the informative function of a lecture with the pleasure of an hour spent in close proximity to extraordinary holdings of paintings, sculpture and artefacts from civilizations past. Viewing artwork from previous centuries, whether Classical Greek or Italian Renaissance or 12th-century Persian, accompanied by a chamber orchestra interpreting music from the period and place, or a dance company responding to its rituals, both expands the viewer's experience and concentrates their attention, providing a richness of involvement for the museum visitor that is only now being recognized and incorporated into the programming, marketing, branding and visitor services of the 21st-century museum. Such examination of the ways in which perceptions can be shifted, ideas translated, and concepts and aesthetics of artwork appreciated by a broad cross section of viewers is extending the function of the museum as well as its basic architecture as an arrangement of galleries and exhibition halls.

The new museum is a meeting place for the gathering of large crowds; it has portals and platforms for watching at a distance or engaging with artists close up, white spaces for hanging solid objects that can also be repurposed for dance, black boxes that are wired for sound and light with moveable parts to be altered according to customized specifications of each consecutive installation or performance, and proscenium theatres for film and lectures, with attached greenrooms and technical facilities. Such features are transforming museums from the contemplative edifices of the past into lively cultural hubs for multimedia actions of all sorts, anticipating future generations whose cultural references will have been shaped by a media-driven world, their knowledge acquired digitally from infinitely linked resources.

Chapter 1, *Performance as Visual Art*, focuses on the work of visual artists whose powerful performances are integral to their overall oeuvre. It shows the work of a generation of artists whose material since the late 1970s has consistently used performance as one of many media for expressing complex content, about both society and the functioning of art and museums within it, giving as much weight to the stylistic signature of the work as to its subjects. It also considers the

PAWEŁ ALTHAMER
Queen Mother of Reality, *2013.*
Commission for Performa 13, New York.
Photo by Paula Court.

aesthetic influence that live performance since that time has had on video and film, in such a way as to make these media inseparable. Indeed, the history of artists' video in the 21st century has a great deal to do with the structure and evolution of artists' performance, particularly in terms of close-up focus on the body, spatial configurations and durational non-narrative material. Attention to these elements can reveal a kind of filmic 'solidification' of performance, where work begins as performance yet ends up as film. The final product, with camerawork that moves around figures and into spaces between them, conjures the atmosphere of a live performance, as though being on set is 'the main event' and the film is the capturing and reimagining of the live work after the fact. Inside the editing process, the artist-director heightens the dramatic juxtaposition of assembled objects, bodies and music, and further articulates the separate parts of the performance, creating a visual assemblage unlike anything seen in traditional narrative films. Thus, the artist controls the roving eye of the viewer, specifying particular angles and approaches, even as he or she manipulates the colour palette, lighting and pacing to create an original and highly textured cinematic experience. Within these films, performers, not actors, are one element among many, to be rearranged in the editing process as needed. Such work requires an elaborate synthesis of the mindsets appropriate to film, visual art and live performance; a combination of expertise and sensibilities taken from all three.

Highly visual and mostly without words, performance is especially suited to communicating cultural differences in the high-tech and much-mediated matrix of online life, and does so across language barriers and geographic borders. Given the inherent narratives implied by live performance – because every individual body tells a story – it is also surprisingly accessible. For artists from countries outside the major art centres, from places as disparate as Bangladesh, Russia and South Africa, it serves as a passport to the international art arena that would be somewhat more elusive for an artist

↓
RALPH LEMON
Untitled, *2010.*
Archival pigment print from original film.
Little Yazoo, Mississippi.

SARAH MICHELSON
Devotion Study #1 – The American Dancer, *2012.*
Whitney Museum of American Art, New York.
Photo by Paula Court.

CANDICE BREITZ
New York, New York, *2009.*
Commission for Performa with Kunsthaus Bregenz,
produced in association with The Power Plant and Scott
Macaulay, New York.
Photo by Paula Court.

working in painting or sculpture. Chapter 2, *World Citizenship: Performance as a Global Language,* describes greatly varied performances from around the globe, situating the material in its original context, while explaining the ways in which its use of the body, local rituals and customs, music, costumes and objects, give the work an eloquence and insistent relevance that makes it possible to transfer ideas and sensibilities far beyond the place of origin.

Chapter 3, *Radical Action: On Performance and Politics,* continues the exploration of performance as a highly flexible and expressive medium for deeply felt content. World citizenry and other humanist concerns lie at the heart of much of the work emerging from countries where war has been a continuous backdrop for many decades. This chapter looks at the ways in which artists working amid day to day turmoil use the multi-layered nature of performance to record shifting political templates, and how they engage the international art platform for making their aesthetically charged and emotional reflections widely known.

Chapter 4, *Dance After Choreography,* provides background to the recent upsurge of interest among museums and galleries in showing contemporary dance, that began in 2007 with several timed exhibitions, Documenta and the Performa Biennial, which included significant programming of avant-garde dance. Key figures from 1960s and '70s New York, when the downtown art and dance worlds were inextricably linked, have been the focus of much recent interest, and are often presented alongside a younger generation of intellectually astute choreographers, both in the US and in France and Germany, who in many ways continue the trajectory of their ideas. This chapter will provide an overview of the interplay between European and American contemporary dance – a transatlantic dialogue that is spearheading new levels of 'conceptual dance' while engaging with material from Nigeria, Central Africa and South Africa that is also part of the postmodern dance conversation.

Chapter 5, *Off Stage: New Theatre,* begins with a comparative exploration of why performance art is not theatre. Until recently, there has been very little interest shown between practitioners from each side in the other's work. For artists who view performance through a visual lens, and playwrights and directors for whom the text might be the first point of departure, the crossover has been minimal. In the last few years, however, visual artists have been using the stage as a means of focusing their audiences frontally on works designed for the proscenium, while theatre artists are using the blank slate of the 'white cube' in a museum or gallery to deconstruct the elements of theatre. This chapter shows how each side is finally taking note of the other, while the dividing line of text keeps the two separated in parallel but distinct worlds.

Chapter 6, *Performing Architecture,* describes a burgeoning interest among a generation of architects in considering the meticulous methods of architecture – building spaces for people to move through, act upon, and act within – as essentially methods of performance. Considering how spaces are felt and how participants within their parameters are transformed into performers, this expanded awareness of the theatre of constructed spaces is shaping both education and sensibilities in architecture today. Rooted in the politically engaged 'conceptual architecture' of the post-'68 generation, 'architecture as performance' has grown as a theoretical discourse as much as a practical application. Interaction inside and around built spaces is also of interest to visual artists who use the tools of architecture to articulate special parameters, whether behavioural, anthropological or perceptual. This chapter will review the urban activism that has emerged alongside the idea of architecture as performance, showing a broad range of investigative experimentation by individual architects and collectives. 'Oppositional architecture', 'slow architecture' and 'psycho buildings' are some of the subsets of architecture as discursive process used by architects and artists alike.

Compressing time and layers of information into a single publication provides its own structural demands. Are these images best considered as a storyboard for a documentary film, each a window into a visual world of live performance? Or should they be viewed as one might a shard of pottery from another civilization; a starting point in a much longer trail? Photographs of performance carry within them stories and aesthetic variants that are each artist's own; they are above all arrangements by visual artists, and it is the artist's singular style and worldview that such photographs convey. The photographer, as mediator and recorder, captures the work of and for each artist, and in the process produces a genre of photography unlike any other. This material cannot simply be considered 'documentation', as though the action just happened to be caught on camera, outside of the artist's design. Rather, the photographs in this book are to be read, detail for detail, for colour, composition, rhythm and content, as one would the elements of a painting or sculpture. In telling us something about the complicated context in which each performance was made, they are essential references in contemporary art history.

As a platform for the examined life, from multiple viewpoints and in many registers, performance draws filmmakers as well as playwrights, choreographers, composers, architects and designers into its avant-garde realm. It offers a license for untrammelled invention, and its study necessarily encompasses a plurality of histories, and an understanding of where these intersect. This book approaches intersections between performance art and film, between art and theatre, between dance in the dance world and dance in the art world, between architecture as building and architecture as experience. Overall, the material offers readings of a vastly and rapidly changing society. With each visual clue and accompanying caption, an artist can be seen to render a fragment of the humanism we seek, their insights and sensibilities making us more alert to our endlessly shifting world.

CHAPTER 1

Performance as Visual Art

Endymion, *2013.*
Commission for Performa 13,
Swiss Institute, New York.
Photo by Paula Court.

I n 2002, one year after the tragedy of September 11 in New York, Marina Abramović staged a memorial for the wounded city: *The House with the Ocean View.* A work of meditation and direct engagement with the public, it provided a quiet gathering place for viewers from ten in the morning to midnight for twelve days. Inside the large white gallery where she would live on a platform, built 2 metres (6 ft) above ground and reachable only by step ladders with rungs made of butcher's knives, Abramović went through the motions of a day: she sat at a table, she drank water, she showered, she changed clothes, she slept on a wooden pallet. For long periods of time she stood facing forward, making eye contact, sometimes for as long as thirty to forty minutes, with people who came to watch and wait in silence with her. It was a work of surprising beauty. Elegant and sparse, the clean lines of the furnishings underlined the volumes of the space, generating a quiet rhythm from surface to surface. The triptych of partitioned 'rooms' suspended along the back wall, representing bathroom, living room and bedroom of the house with the ocean view, had the formal proportions of an altarpiece, while a few touches of colour – of the artist's dark hair, of her primary colour workman-like clothing – gave painterly detail to a space shaped with the formal restraint of a minimalist sculptor.

The House with the Ocean View was a summation of Abramović's work as both visual artist and performance artist. Its visual impact showed her understanding of the relationships of built forms, of sculpture and design, alongside her demonstrated ability as a live performer. That she manipulated imagery and performance elements with such expertise showed an artist in full control of her material and her aesthetic. She had conceived and built a perfect container for her performance – both a frame and a pedestal for an art that was as intensely visual as it was visceral. Through eye contact she anchored each viewer in place, establishing the physical presence of the artist as the focal point linking the work's various parts and reinforcing ideas about the audience as participant and as witness, while also providing an elegantly beautiful setting for their shared experience.

Abramović's *House with the Ocean View,* and the increasing number of other performances that took place in the opening years of the new millennium – Vanessa Beecroft's *VB 42 Intrepid,* 2000, Shirin Neshat's *Logic of the Birds,* 2001, or Catherine Sullivan's *Five Economies (Big Hunt/Little Hunt),* 2003, to name a few – marked a turning point for performance art. Rich in content and complex in iconography, these works were also irresistible to look at. Loaded with meaning, the material was as sophisticated and aesthetically exhilarating as the best artwork being made in the 2000s in film, photography and video installation. Steve McQueen, Gillian Wearing, Douglas Gordon, Sam Taylor-Wood, Stan Douglas, Dominique Gonzalez-Foerster, Eija-Liisa Ahtila, Yang Fudong, Thomas Demand, Bill Viola and William Kentridge each made work that in scale and imagery, as well as structure and pacing, looked a lot like live performance transposed to film. Projected life size or larger onto long walls in a gallery or museum, many of these films were shot amid intricately constructed sets or on locations where the action was made up of visually compelling tableaus and mostly wordless performances. Matthew Barney's *Cremaster* series, 1997–2002; Isaac Julien's *Vagabondia,* 2000;

Pierre Huyghe's *Streamside Day Follies,* 2003; Douglas Gordon's *Play Dead; Real Time,* 2003; Paul McCarthy's *Pirates,* 2004; Mike Kelley's *Day is Done,* 2005; or Laurie Simmons' *Music of Regret,* 2005, each provided a landscape of never-before-seen imagery that had been constructed as a sequence of live, non-narrative scenes that would become a delirium of unexpected pictures in the process of transposing from one medium to another. While they could be 'read' as film, they could also be viewed as stylized performances. For Pierre Huyghe, his films transposed the ephemeral event of performance to a more permanent medium. 'All my work is performance,' he said. 'Film is just a way of holding onto them and making them solid.'

The performances and performance-films of these artists are some of the finest examples of the highly mediated artwork of the first decade of the 21st century. Visually seductive, their cinematic surfaces were produced by state-of-the-art camerawork and editing. With a focus on figuration and composition, their aesthetics had more to do with a late 20th-century history of visual art and artists' performance than with the history of cinema. Their cameras seemed to be framing and following the bodies of performers precisely in order to make expansive, elegantly composed cinematic landscapes rather than to create character or narrative. That this material appealed to a broad spectrum of audiences had a lot to do with the irresistible quality of film itself. Illuminated surfaces gave an all-encompassing pictorial effect, and the impact of being close up to the installation offered a visceral, 'you-can-step-into-this-film' quality that involved the viewer more directly than the experience of cinema. The video projections of a decade or so earlier had inevitably been less pristine and enticing, made as they were with the more limited technologies available at that time. Installations fitted well into the spaces of the new museums that had been designed with a nod to the capacious live-in lofts and loft-like galleries of the 1970s, with their extended horizontal to vertical ratio. These proportions allowed viewers to take in expansive

MARINA ABRAMOVIĆ
The Artist is Present, *2010.*
Museum of Modern Art, New York.
Photo by Marco Anelli.

projections stretching over many feet, while the process of
watching, whether standing, seated, lying down or walking
across a space from one gallery to the next, became integral
to the experience of the work itself.

Such watching, of the artwork and of audience members
across a room, made for a new kind of self-conscious viewing
among gallery-goers; they shared an active engagement with
the work and with each other, collectively witnessing an event
but participating in it too. They might settle in for hours
to feel the full duration of time inside their own minds and
bodies as specified by the artist, as with Abramović's *House,*
or they might move from space to space in various parts of a
building, as in Francesco Vezzoli's *Right You Are (If You Think
You Are)*, 2007, which took place simultaneously throughout
the Guggenheim Museum, in the ground-floor rotunda, on
the spiralling ramps and also in the below-ground auditorium.
In Jesper Just's *True Love is Yet to Come*, 2005, audiences stood
in front of a small stage that resembled an over-scaled puppet
theatre set in a large white gallery. They leaned up against high
tables scattered across the room, moved closer to the stage or
farther away, finding vantage points during the performance
from which to view the work, rather than being confined
to a single position, as would be the case in a conventional

↑
ROBIN RHODE
Arnold Schönberg's Erwatung, *2015.*
Commission for Performa 15,
Times Square, New York.
Photo by Paula Court.

MARINA ABRAMOVIĆ
Seven Easy Pieces: performing Joseph
Beuys, *How to Explain Pictures to a Dead Hare*
(1965), 2005. 5th of 7 performances. Part of first
*Performa Biennial, Frank Lloyd Wright rotunda,
Guggenheim Museum, New York.*

theatre. In Olafur Eliasson's *The Weather Project,* 2003, an elaborate construction in the vast Turbine Hall at Tate Modern, hundreds of people came daily to watch the progress of a giant circle of orange light mimicking the arc of the sun in its diurnal trek across the sky. Some lay on the floor, others leaned up against walls, others sat cross-legged in circles of friends. They could have been at a summer rock concert in Hyde Park, so informal and spontaneous was their willingness to join in the experience of the crowd. With Carsten Höller's *Test Site,* 2006, installed at Tate Modern, audiences donned crash helmets and protective elbow and knee pads to fall feet-first through a curling metal tube-like sculpture that dropped the viewer very rapidly from a second-floor landing into the Turbine Hall below.

Such events reflected the changing role of the 21st-century museum, which had been transformed since the opening of Tate Modern in the year 2000 from an institution of quiet contemplation and conservation into a cultural pleasure palace of engagement on a blockbuster scale. Designed with halls big enough to accommodate large crowds, the new spaces demanded an equivalent scale of performance to be staged for powerful visual as well as experiential effect. Performance programmes would become regular fare, and by the end of the decade, new performance art departments, curatorial staff and registrars, as well as technical facilities, lighting and sound equipment, and dedicated black-box spaces that could be adjusted to all kinds of staged endeavours were added to the checklists of new museums being readied for the second decade of the millennium. More and more the museum curator would take on the role of commissioner and producer, working hand in hand with artists

to realize cross-disciplinary and multimedia works that not only reflected the mediated world of the time, but also the needs of museums constantly to entice a generation of viewers expecting cultural experience to be as fast-paced and as easily accessible as the smartphones and computers that animated their lives day to day.

The regularity of performance events throughout the calendar year, and the first ever performance art biennial, Performa, dedicated to the history of artists' performance as much as to the commissioning of new work for the 21st century, began to build a repertoire and a reference bank of material within institutions for comparative study and critique. In contrast to the intermittent appearance of performance in the 20th-century museum, and the surprise factor for viewers whenever they encountered such events, performance by the end of the first decade of the 21st century had become widely accepted as standard museum fare. The historical credibility conferred by the institution underlined the intellectual and aesthetic content of artists' performance, while the choice selection of material from a sprawling and generally little-known history made performance that much more palatable in the museum setting. For the many curators, art historians and critics who had never previously considered performance's role in shaping the history of 20th-century art, encountering this material in the museum provided the opportunity to accumulate knowledge and find a language for describing performance that would change the conversation about live art and its role in contemporary art in the most profound ways.

The history of performance itself became exhibition material, with reconstructions of past performances forming a genre all its own. Group 'exhibitions' of re-performed pieces from the past, such as *A Little Bit of History Revisited* in 2001 in Berlin, and *A Short History of Performance* in London in 2002, and exhibitions by solo artists, such as Marina Abramović's *Seven Easy Pieces* in New York in 2005, as well as Allan Kaprow's *18 Happenings in Six Parts* by dancers, students and trained performers in Munich and New York in 2009, were highly visible events that together indicated a new investigative approach to ephemeral performance material from the past. These thoughtful and carefully constructed productions, executed with sensitivity and appreciable awareness of the paradox of re-performing material that had intentionally been performed only once or twice when originally conceived, provided a means to revisit and invoke the political and cultural ethos of the times in which they were made. This 'restored' history proved of considerable interest to artists, curators and students alike, but also to the general museum-going public, who responded with interest to the conceptual intentions behind each performance that was being explained and presented to them, and to the opportunity to be in close proximity to the artists themselves. They were curious, as were the specialists, to catch up on material that was being treated as a modern archaeological 'find' in art history. As old performances were uncovered, dusted off, and displayed in the pristine halls of the museum, audiences were ready to follow the pedagogical reasoning of the art historians and curators mounting this work. Articulating the history of performance became a priority in art museums, which in turn raised questions of preservation and conservation. Registrars examined the work being brought into museums, some to join their permanent collections, and devised methods for recording and notating artists' living wills in terms of how they would wish such projects to be maintained and re-performed in the future. It also became evident that many museums already had extensive holdings in performance, albeit archived under another name. Drawings, collages, photographs, videos, films and even paintings made for or about performance were acknowledged for what they were, and in many instances were reassigned to the performance art departments.

The first decade of the millennium saw an accumulation of entirely new possibilities for performance by visual artists, both conceptually and aesthetically. Work by Abramović, Kentridge, Sullivan, Barney, Just, Vezzoli, Beecroft, Alÿs, Huyghe, Allora and Calzadilla, Tino Sehgal, Gonzalez-Foerster, John Bock, and Zhang Huan among many others, introduced a level of expertise and command of material that was increasingly sophisticated and polished. Production values and a keen awareness of the relationship of performer to audience became integral to material that was simultaneously expanding in scope and ambition. Elmgreen and Dragset's *Drama Queens,* 2005, took place on a proscenium stage in a traditional theatre and included motorized pedestals supporting larger than life-size replicas of sculptures by Barbara Hepworth, Alberto Giacometti, Jeff Koons and Andy Warhol, careening around one another as directed by off-stage handlers with wireless transmitters; Matthew Barney's *KHU, Act Two of Ancient Evenings,* 2010, for an outdoor audience that included a video screening in the Detroit Museum of Art, chartered buses to an abandoned glue factory on the Rouge River, and a ride upstream on a barge. These highly produced, beautifully rendered productions raised the bar of expectation for a medium that had long been considered outside the reach of critical assessment and peripheral to the main business of art. Performance artists were now expected to make objects that could hold up to ongoing scrutiny over time. With this new work that was increasingly dense with content, and demanded close attention on the part of viewers, the argument that performance was difficult to incorporate into contemporary art history or into the collection of a museum because of its ephemeral nature became irrelevant. The more prolonged the time spent with a work, the more evident its conceptual complexity, the easier it became to accept performance as critical to an artist's overall oeuvre, and to the overall discussion of contemporary art. Performance was seen to be a nuanced artistic practice capable of simultaneously conveying layers of meaning in intensely visual and visceral ways. It was finally accepted as integral to museum programming and a precedent was set for a new generation of artists who would be entirely comfortable with creating live art expressly for the museum context.

VANESSA BEECROFT
VB55, 2005.
Neue Nationalgalerie, Berlin.

Known for an intriguing and contentious use of the female nude as a medium for confrontation, Vanessa Beecroft toys with the boundaries of empowerment and abjection in *VB55*. In April 2005, one hundred women stood in tight formation inside the glass box that is Mies van der Rohe's Neue Nationalgalerie in Berlin, transforming the structure with its glass curtain facade into a giant vitrine and allowing a curious public to peer inside from the street, to stare and wonder at the women. Wearing nothing but flesh-coloured nylon leggings and slathered in almond oil, the women are at once inanimate mannequins and Aphrodites, girls-next-door and Barbies lined up against a giant display case. Their nudity is transformed into a kind of art-historical catwalk, drawing on painting, sculpture and pop cultural references from antiquity to Titian to contemporary culture. Carefully documented in both video and photography for future exhibition, archiving and sale, *VB55* is an exercise in the aesthetics of 'product', creating material for visual and cultural consumption and daring its audience to stare for an extended period of time at the living goods on display.

MATTHEW BARNEY
KHU, *2010*.
Act from River of Fundament, *Detroit.*
Photos by Hugo Glendinning.

Ancient Evenings was a set of performances staged and filmed in collaboration with Jonathan Bepler to create the 6-hour-long operatic film, *River of Fundament*. Each act is loosely based on Norman Mailer's 1983 novella of the same name, and each tackles a different stage of the soul's transformation from death to rebirth, in accordance with Mailer's contemporary retelling of Egyptian mythology. In Act II, *KHU*, the artists' pit stop is Detroit where, at an abandoned glue factory, assembly-line machinists turn steel sheets into sixteen working viols. These are played in a mournful aria before blues singer Belita Woods belts out incantations from the Egyptian Book of the Dead. A small audience, packed on to a barge that floats down the Rouge and Detroit rivers, stumbles upon a crime-scene investigation. As four towboats loaded with musicians circle the barge, the cadaver of the Chrysler from *REN*, a previous act that took place in Los Angeles, is pulled from the river. After sunset the audience watches as the car's body is cut into pieces that are melted into liquid, to be incorporated into a future chapter.

RYAN MCNAMARA
MEEM: A Story Ballet About the Internet, *2013.*
Commission for Performa 13, Connelly Theater, New York.

Exploring the highly interconnected networks of popular meaning and reference that course through the internet, Ryan McNamara's *MEEM* is a performance of seventeen choreographed tableaus that play inside a theatre's auditorium, corridors, music pit, stage and stair wells in homage to the boundless momentum of free, open and immediate sharing of information online. Borrowing conventions from music, film and television, the highly mediated dances overlap each other, sending the audience's attention in all directions as stage hands wheel each viewer's seat on specially devised 'people movers' to different 'staging areas' throughout the theatre. Combining complex choreography with references to popular culture, *MEEM* is a pastiche of cultural systems that course through McNamara's other works.

PAUL MCCARTHY
Piccadilly Circus, *2003.*
Installation view, Hauser & Wirth, London.

Set in the tense political climate of the months preceding the
Iraq War, this volatile, slapstick encounter between caricatures of
George W. Bush, Osama bin Laden and multiple iterations of the
Queen Mother is an irreverent nod to the violence of impending
war. In a chaotically furnished beaux-arts building, amid oversized
sculptures and large-scale video projections, grotesquely costumed
actors destroy their own bodily integrity and that of their fellow
players, punching, hacking and tearing away at their foam heads,
force-feeding and struggling against each other in a frenzied
scene that might at a glance be mistaken for a manic children's
television show. McCarthy's powerful political critique explores
power and grandiosity via the exaggerated colours and gestures of
Hollywood-style make-believe.

SHIRIN NESHAT
Logic of the Birds, *2001*.
LEFT *performance at The Kitchen, New York.*
BELOW LEFT *film still from triptych.*

Shirin Neshat's first work of live
art adapts the poetry of 12th-century
Persian mystic Farid ud-Din Attar into a
contemporary dreamscape of painted hills
and valleys, weaving an arduous and surreal
narrative as 'thirty birds in search of a leader
risk life and limb, traverse fire, flood and
drought'. A triptych of exquisite films sets
the stage. On the edge of a lake in upstate
New York and on specially painted terrain in
Pennsylvania, thirty chador-clad performers,
led by Iranian singer Sussan Deyhim, 'walk
off' the screens onto the stage in a remarkable
melding of live performance and projection.
Inhabiting the space between fantasy and
reality, here and there, then and now, the
production wordlessly communicates how,
in the protagonists' longing for direction, all
are leaders and all are followers. Performance
offers Neshat a chance to immerse viewers
in the complex politics of her visual and
intellectual content.

ROMAN ONDÁK
Measuring the Universe, *2007.*
Museum of Modern Art, New York.

Set in a stark, white gallery, Roman Ondák's *Measuring the Universe* takes its audience as subject and object. Tracings of each visitor's height are recorded, along with their names and the day's date, in black marker on the gallery walls. Unfolding across the length of the exhibition, the lines progressively clutter the gallery, overlapping and rendering each other illegible. Each measure, anonymous and uniform, serves as a placeholder for the thousands of individuals who visit, such that they fill the room across time and space. Nobody who enters ever leaves.

↑

AÏDA RUILOVA
The Silver Globe, *2007*.
For Performa 07, The Kitchen, New York.

Aïda Ruilova's *The Silver Globe* takes direct inspiration from the cult 1988 Polish science-fiction film of the same name. Created during a period of time when sci-fi was approached as an escapist genre in Polish cinema, the film tells the story of space colonists who leave Earth in search of freedom. The eventual failure of the space mission portrayed, and the primitive moon society spawned from its various survivors, work in various ways as allegories for the Soviet programme installed at the time. In Ruilova's performance, live music, dance, sculptural props and original video overlay excerpts from the original film, weaving together a dark, whimsical and hallucinatory experience in an allegory of Cold War history and politics.

←

JOHN BOCK
Boxer, *2002*.
Film stills. Berlin.

Known for a spectacular and chaotic visual language that reconstitutes sculpture and film into staged actions, layered installations and elegantly collaged wall hangings, John Bock casts his absurdist lens on boxing in this early work, capturing the collision of comedy and violence in one 2-minute video. Costumed in clownish ensembles with food-stuffed appendages, Bock and his opponent throw punches with increasing frenzy until they are entirely undone, smashing heads that spill cauliflower into the ring and spatter red cabbage across the walls. Referencing Dada and classic Hollywood comic performers, including Buster Keaton and Harpo Marx, Bock's visually arresting sets reveal the theatricality in painting, sculpture and film, as media combine deliciously in his complete version of the 'total artwork'.

ADAM PENDLETON

The Revival, *2007*.
Commission for Performa 07, New York.
RIGHT *promotional screen print.*
BELOW *performance at Stephan Weiss Studios, New York.*
Photos by Paula Court.

Adam Pendleton's first full-scale live performance fused
the disjunctive genres of Southern-style religious revival
and avant-garde spoken word poetry. Centred on a podium
in the role of 'preacher' and flanked by two bandstands
on which a thirty-person gospel choir is divided, the artist
delivers a secular revival with ecstatic religious fervour. The
words come not from biblical texts but from a compilation
of experimental writing – Pendleton's own as well as those
of Larry Kramer, Leslie Scalapino, John Ashbery, Jesse
Jackson and Howard Barker. With 'testimonials' from Liam
Gillick and Jena Osman, the whole was underscored by the
original music and performance of jazz composer and pianist
Jason Moran, and set the bar for the exacting language and
intellectual content of his work in other media.

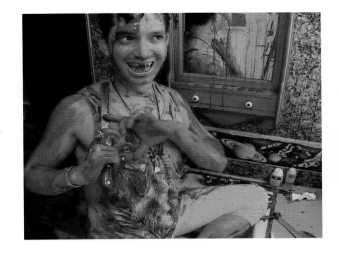

RYAN TRECARTIN
A Family Finds Entertainment, *2004.*
Film stills.

Trecartin's camp epic chronicles the story of a manic teenager named Skippy, played by the artist, and his absurdist and existential struggle to come out to his family and friends, hiding himself in a literal closet. Drawing complex and obscure references from philosophy and popular culture, the delirious 40-minute film weaves hyperactive narrative threads that interrupt and cross each other, disorienting the viewer with bursts of visual effect and animation. The desperate melodrama of the characters' lives, punctuated by clownish violence, creates a portrait – as does much of Trecartin's work – of a generation both validated and hopelessly damaged by media bombardment, unable to escape its constant self-reference.

ROBIN RHODE
Promenade, 2008.
36 C-prints face-mounted with Plexiglass on aluminium panels.
Panels, each: 53.3 x 35.6 cm (21 x 40 in.).
Tucci Russo Studio per l'Arte Contemporanea, Torre Pellice.

Berlin-based South African artist Robin Rhode invents a
highly imaginative visual language where graffiti and sidewalk chalk
drawings intersect. Produced through fast-paced performances,
wall drawings become make-believe objects: a bicycle that the
artist pretends to mount, a grand piano that he pretends to play.
The total work is captured in serial photographs and stop-motion
videos before being painted over again. *Promenade* was performed on
an interior wall in a gallery in Turin as part of a body of work that
would become the visual component for a concert of Mussorgsky's
Pictures at an Exhibition the following year. The performer, dressed
in a business suit and white gloves, 'enters' a shower of geometric
abstract chalk shapes in a humorous push-and-pull as they appear
(and disappear) magically from his hand. The impression is of an
artist who is both master of and subject to his own creative process.

DOMINIQUE GONZALEZ-FOERSTER & ARI BENJAMIN MEYERS

K.62/K.85, 2009.
Commission for Performa 09, Abrons Arts Center, New York.
Photo by Paula Court.

The complementary pieces K.62 and K.85 were a series of diverging and then converging experiences – interactive and serendipitous performances that, for the audience, began before they set foot in the theatre. At the ticket booth, visitors are given the choice between two tickets. Those with tickets reading 'K.62' are shown to a Lower East Side theatre where films are screened and fictional production assistants on walkie-talkies track the locations of persons referred to as 'K's. Those with 'K.85' tickets are led on a scripted journey around lower Manhattan, stopping at scenes from Martin Scorsese's film *After Hours*, and finally trickling into the large theatre through an onstage door until all are accounted for. Each audience is the other's show, unaware of the separate journeys they will take.

CANDICE BREITZ
New York, New York, 2009.
Commission for Performa 09, Abrons Arts Center, New York.
Photo by Paula Court.

Video and installation artist Candice Breitz presented
her first ever live performance, *New York, New York*, as part of
Performa 09, creating a remarkable work that mimicked the
tight editing process of the fast-paced videos for which she
is known. Working with four sets of identical twins, Breitz
created two casts of actors (each from a pair of twins), and in
intensive character development sessions asked each pair to
work on a single fictional character. The result was an evening
of improvised performance on a stage-set dressed as though
for a popular soap opera, loaded with twin motifs, such as a
double portrait of Elvis. The performers probed sameness,
difference and the fragile condition of individuality, creating
on set an ambiguous 'scripted life' – another powerful theme
in Breitz's oeuvre.

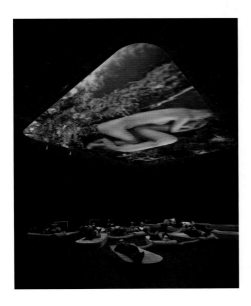

PIPILOTTI RIST
Homo Sapiens Sapiens, *2005*.
Video installation. Louisiana Museum of Modern Art, Humlebæk.
Photo by Paul Bouchard.

Since the 1980s Pipilotti Rist has constructed vibrant, hypnotic video art and multimedia installations, creating mesmerizing environments that consider voyeurism, the treatment of the female body, and the physical engagement of audiences in art. Sprawled across the ceiling of the Louisiana Museum of Modern Art's Hall Gallery, *Homo Sapiens Sapiens* invites viewers to lie on bright oval beds and look up at kaleidoscopic projections – soft scenes of nature and open skies. A woman floats through the images, splitting and twisting as though directed by external forces. The saturated images and distorted body produce a scene of bizarre, unsettling familiarity.

CORY ARCANGEL
Bruce Springsteen 'Born to Run'
Glockenspiel Addendum, *2008*.
Light Industry, Brooklyn.

Cory Arcangel's irreverent project is a full glockenspiel accompaniment, composed, played and recorded by the artist, to Bruce Springsteen's canonical 1975 album *Born to Run*. Exercising an informal authorial control of the Springsteen album, Arcangel overlays the glockenspiel on all but the three songs that already feature the instrument. This audacious play with the popular is central to Arcangel's body of work, where celebrity, pop music, and allusions to video games and the internet are brought together to recombine wholly familiar scenes and render them new.

LAURIE SIMMONS
The Music of Regret, *2005.*
Film stills. Act III commission with Salon 94 for
Performa 05, New York.

A mini-musical presented in three acts, *The Music of Regret*
is in many ways an extension of Laurie Simmons' canonical
photographic work, where dolls, collectors' miniatures and
children's toys become the unlikely protagonists of desperate
domestic scenes recalling the family life and catalogue images
of the 1960s. Simmons' first foray into moving image work,
shot in 35mm film and spanning 40 minutes, *The Music of
Regret* brings her small-scale props to human proportions,
presenting life-sized puppets and dummies – an overgrown
toy gun, a doll's house, a pocket watch – that share in very
human expressions of family conflict, lost romance and the
longing to be noticed.

ELAINE STURTEVANT
Spinoza in Las Vegas, *2009.*
Performed as part of UBS Openings: Saturday Live,
Tate Modern, London.

The first theatre piece by American artist Elaine Sturtevant, *Spinoza in Las Vegas* presents the unlikely adventures of 17th-century Dutch rationalist philosopher Baruch Spinoza as a character radically displaced in the postmodern landscape of today. Known for his writings positing that true perfection is found only in reality, Spinoza, played by Sturtevant, finds himself in the highly commercial and artificial reality of Las Vegas, where hotels and attractions fantastically simulate places and environments from the pyramids in Luxor to Classical Rome. Sturtevant, recognized since the mid-1960s for her appropriative art, comments here on the nature of authorship, questioning the truth of reality and the invention of its replica.

CARSTEN HÖLLER
Mirror Carousel, 2005.
Installation view. New Museum, New York.

Carsten Höller's *Mirror Carousel* is a functional, large-scale, interactive carousel with surfaces lined in mirrors, inviting visitors to a slow-turning ride that is equal parts opulence and whimsy. Nodding towards the vanity of participation, *Mirror Carousel* allows the audience to watch themselves see and experience, reflecting their presence and collaboration back at themselves and others in the room. Höller deploys this piece as a means of altering the audience's physical and psychological associations with common experiences – in this case that of the carnival – inspired by his training as a scientist to experiment with variables of cause and effect.

PAWEŁ ALTHAMER
Common Task, 2009.
Brussels.

Fashioning a live sculpture of living, breathing and moving participants, Paweł Althamer's ambitious project *Common Task* transplanted 150 of the artist's friends and neighbours from their community in Warsaw to locations across the world, exploring transience, otherness and what it means to belong to a place or nationality. Outfitted in gold spacesuits that draw visual allusions to science fiction, and transported in a golden Boeing 737 of Althamer's design, the cohort is made alien by the peculiarity of its appearance, participating in social actions and interactive performances in Brasília, Brussels, Mali and Oxford that recontextualize daily life in terms of the unexpected.

MARINA ABRAMOVIĆ
The House with the Ocean View, 2002.
Sean Kelly Gallery, New York.
Photo by Attilio Maranzano.

Throughout a career of more than four decades,
which began in the 1960s in war-torn Yugoslavia,
Marina Abramović has created psychologically
and physically challenging work that often takes
inspiration from traditions of meditation from around
the world. As with her early explorations of the
boundaries of body and mind as a way to understand
social conflicts, Abramović's iconic *House with the Ocean
View* was a response to a particular event and place:
New York City after 9/11. 'People were more emotional,
more vulnerable, more spiritual,' she said. 'The idea for
this work was an experiment...to find a rigorous way of
living, of purification, to change the attitude of people
who came to see me. Some came for two minutes,
others stayed for three, four hours.' For twelve days
she lived in the gallery, in full public view on a raised
platform indicating domestic areas for sleeping,
bathing and lounging. She showered, drank water
and moved from one 'room' to the other, but for long
stretches of time she sat and looked directly at people,
making eye contact and creating a web of empathy
between strangers.

PHILIPPE PARRENO AND RIRKRIT TIRAVANIJA
Puppets, 2006.
Installation view. Friedrich Petzel Gallery, New York.

A group of five puppets representing Philippe Parreno, Rirkrit
Tiravanija, Pierre Huyghe, Liam Gillick and Hans Ulrich Obrist
prepare to watch a film featuring each puppet figure in a panel
discussion on a new book by Obrist entitled *Interviews*, supposedly
published a year earlier. Originally convened as a live interview
with just two puppets and a ventriloquist to perform a scripted
dialogue with Obrist, exploring ideas of memory, theatricality
and human interaction, the five artists each used their childlike
characters as vehicles to expand the conversation, including personal
comments and anecdotes. Parreno's alter-ego was also his own
argumentative interlocutor, while Tiravanija's stand-in served as a
demonstration of 'how individuals can be active contributors to
their own media culture, rather than mere consumers of it.' This
collection of well-known art personalities as puppets has grown over
the years, providing ongoing commentary about the hierarchies and
machinations of art-world and real-world politics.

RINEKE DIJKSTRA
I See a Woman Crying, 2009.
Film still. Tate Liverpool, UK.

Considering the deep and visceral affective potential in a work of art, Rineke Dijkstra's 12-minute video portrait of nine British schoolchildren was filmed in front of Picasso's 1937 painting *Weeping Woman*. Without ever showing the painting – a work of contorted and haunting grief depicted in Cubistic angles – on camera, the children make simple observations that grow into imaginative, descriptive and emotional insights into the life of the work and the woman pictured therein. Following in the artist's visual vocabulary favouring close-up and often life-size portraits, here we are confronted with two: the children as they sit and interact, and the woman we never see.

YANG FUDONG
Seven Intellectuals in a Bamboo Forest, *2007.*
Film still.

Yang Fudong's seminal five-part film references the Seven
Sages – intellectuals from the Wei and Jin Dynasties represented
often in traditional Chinese art. The work has no defined narrative,
existing as a series of tableaus where the figures – five men and two
women – commune with nature and each other, stripping away their
identities and scholarly attributes to transform themselves across
the film's parts into rowdy drunks, naturalists and humble farmers,
eventually being transported through time to modern-day Shanghai.
Here they are overly attended to by the entire staff of a restaurant,
several members of the group passing out from overindulgence.
The work examines individuals' roles in society, cultural norms and
personal desires, weighing pressures to conform against unrestrained
expression. The film looks at the rift between collectivist and
individualist society, evocative of China's current cultural climate,
caught between Maoist communist policy and rampant globalization.

ALLORA & CALZADILLA
Stop, Repair, Prepare: Variations on Ode to Joy No. 1, 2008.
Gladstone Gallery, New York.

From a duo known for their powerfully inventive performances
incorporating sounds as historic and political references, *Stop, Repair, Prepare*
is a deconstructed performance of Beethoven's Ninth Symphony (known
as 'Ode to Joy'), which in 1972 was adopted as the anthem of Europe. This
ambiguous composition, which has long been invoked as a symbol of
humanist values and national pride, is mined for its symbolic as well as
musical references, including John Cage's 'prepared piano'. Sitting inside a
45 cm (18 in.) hole cut out of the body of the piano, a classical pianist leans
over the keyboard, playing upside down and backwards while walking and
pushing the piano across the gallery space. Nudging viewers out of the path
of the piano as she creates an immersive setting for sound and concept.
The result is a structurally incomplete version of the ode – the hole in the
piano renders two octaves inoperative – that fundamentally transforms
both the player/instrument dynamic and the signature melody, disrupting
the famous anthem and its overriding metaphors.

KORAKRIT ARUNANONDCHAI
Painting with history in a room filled with
people with funny names 4, *2017.*
*Performance with Boychild with live music by Aaron David
Ross, light design by Alex Gvojic and programming
by Michael Potvin. Clearing Gallery, Brooklyn.*

Weaving his intimate familial history into urgent critiques
of global capitalism and data collection, sculptor, performer
and video artist Korakrit Arunanondchai creates a haunting,
mangled sci-fi forest growing within a white-walled gallery space.
Collaborating with performance artist Boychild, Arunanondchai
activates a dystopian, wiry installation. Humanoid figures, naked
except for body paint, move through the apocalyptic debris in
primal, contorted motions, light glowing from their mouths.
Illuminated by vibrant, pulsating lasers, with smoke billowing
around them, they emerge from the topography in a scene of
carnal, alien ritual.

NATHALIE DJURBERG
Untitled (Working Title Kids and Dogs), *2007.*
LEFT *documentation of performance.*
BELOW *film still. Commission for Performa 07,*
The Zipper Theater, New York.
Photos by Paula Court.

Nathalie Djurberg's first live work is a two-part
33-minute claymation odyssey, where city streets are the
setting for a violent war between a group of grenade-throwing
children and a pack of pedigree dogs. Scored and played
live on a small stage alongside the screen by Djurberg and
musician Hans Berg, assisted by a collection of homemade
instruments, bags of trash and found objects, the film
culminates in a hospital scene where the wounded, both
human and canine, cry out among the sounds of war –
the militant beating of a bass drum and the noise of gunfire –
and are put together again by overworked doctors and nurses.

PIERRE HUYGHE
Streamside Day, *2003*.
Film stills.

French artist Pierre Huyghe toes the line between
the fictive and the real in *Streamside Day*, a 26-minute film
completely scripted by the artist, who invents both a town
and a ritual for its inhabitants. A development under
construction, the town of Streamside, just north of
New York, becomes the locus of a celebration of transition
from the man-made into nature. A parade, songs, speeches,
costumes and decorations are organized and form a backdrop
to the experience of wilderness. Part-documentary, part-
fantasy, the film contrasts what was and what is, and how
our society and culture have transformed nature, putting
model homes in its place.

GUY BEN-NER

Stealing Beauty, 2007.
Film stills.

Guy Ben-Ner weaves the theatre of
the everyday into this hilarious 18-minute
video revealing a slice of domestic life in
the midst of an ordinary shopping day
at IKEA. With his wife and two young
daughters, Ben-Ner boldly inhabits a display
'bathroom', 'kitchen' and 'bedroom' (each
with price tags still attached to the objects
for sale), acting out everyday interactions in
the rooms of the generic house. Borrowing
from vaudeville and classic American sit-
com, while claiming ownership of these
commercial spaces through his surreptitious
filming, Ben-Ner ironically conflates
consumerist culture and domestic life. The
unofficial film set, appropriated by the artist
without permission, was immediately shut
down the moment authorities discovered
the impromptu performance. The artist
and his family were asked to leave the store.

NICK CAVE

ABOVE HEARD•DAM, *2013. Denver Art Museum.*
LEFT HEARD•NY, *2013. Grand Central Terminal, New York.*
Photos by James Prinz.

Designing surreal, meticulous 'Soundsuits' – found objects
and domestic materials crafted into wearable sculptures
camouflaging race, gender and identity – dancer, costumer
and visual artist Nick Cave unleashed a herd of thirty 'horses'
in the midst of Grand Central Terminal for his performance,
HEARD•NY. Worn by Alvin Ailey dancers and set to the beat
of booming drums, the dazzling costumes were influenced by
African ceremonial costumes, Tibetan embroidery and a range
of global rituals. The vibrant, colourful horses disrupted the
New York transportation hub, inserting international, cross-
cultural politics and histories in a visually joyous, fantastical
interruption of public space.

CHRISTIAN MARCLAY
The Clock, *2010.*
Installation View. White Cube Mason's Yard, London.

Sampling thousands of film excerpts featuring clocks and referencing the passage of time, Christian Marclay's 24-hour film *The Clock* presents a variety of time pieces – from wristwatches to clock towers to digital displays – that show the incremental progression of time, minute by minute and moment by moment. With a technical virtuosity that allowed each snippet to be lifted from its original context and placed cunningly into the time stream of the film, the work presents time itself as a protagonist, monumental and incessant, that paces lives and societies on a grand scale. Set to the unrelenting rhythm of real time, the film shows individuals entering bars, sleeping, waking up, gathering for meals and travelling in vehicles, collaging material in much the same way as his previous video work.

**CHRISTIAN TOMASZEWSKI & JOANNA
MALINOWSKA**
Mother Earth Sister Moon, 2009.
Commission for Performa 09, Chashama 679, New York.
Photo by Paula Court.

Tracing the visual legacy of the 1960s Space Race
throughout the former Communist bloc, Polish artist
Christian Tomaszewski, in collaboration with Joanna
Malinowska, presents a Soviet vision of the future –
a speculative image of Russia's Cold War aspirations. Brought
to life in a futurist fashion show where models wear avant-
garde designs inspired by the unique aesthetics of Eastern
European science fiction and the Soviet space programme,
the work unfolds inside a cosmonaut suit of absurd
proportions, lending its belly as a runway.

EDDIE PEAKE
Endymion, *2013.*
Commission for Performa 13, Swiss Institute, New York.
Photo by Paula Court.

Performing choreography imbued with wild emotion – passion, jealousy, anger and desire – the dancers in Eddie Peake's *Endymion* speak through movement with a physical vocabulary that addresses our most basic and universal instincts and sentiments. Fully painted in either black or gold, the nude performers recall statues from antiquity – Apollos and Aphrodites that pay homage to the eponymous figure from Greek mythology, who seduced the moon with his beauty. Gradually entwining around one another over the course of an hour, the dancers' distinct colours blend, all becoming burnished versions of their former selves, less like sculptures or abstractions as the veneer of perfection strips away.

FRANCESCO VEZZOLI

Right You Are (If You Think You Are), 2007.
Commission for Performa 07, Guggenheim
Museum, New York.
Photo by Paula Court.

Vezzoli's 2007 restaging of Luigi Pirandello's
play in the Guggenheim Museum examines
the allure of celebrity and unstable nature of
personal identity. The script evokes an absent
female character who becomes the obsession of
a group of actors. Fuelled by rumour and gossip,
they manically dissect her attributes, and the
frenzied narrative becomes increasingly obscure
as the woman is continually redefined by the
group's most recent allegations. The cast is itself
made up of noted celebrities, including Cate
Blanchett, Helen Mirren and Natalie Portman,
implicating the audience in its very dissection of
celebrity-mongering.

LIAM GILLICK

Three Perspectives and a Short Scenario |
Mirrored Image: A 'Volvo' Bar, *2008.*
Kunstverein Munich.

A 'Volvo' Bar transformed Kunstverein Munich into
an active installation that incorporated twenty years of
Gillick's work. Collaborating with a group of young Munich
actors, the script was developed into a series of performances
that took place within the exhibition. Later transferred to
Eastside Projects in Birmingham, Gillick's eight-act play
continued to adapt the exhibition space as a stage on which
social phenomena of a post-industrial society can be played
out. The negotiation of models of communality, a core aspect
of Gillick's mise-en-scène, is explored via reference to the loss
of car manufacturing in Birmingham in recent decades.

CHRISTIAN JANKOWSKI
Rooftop Routine, *2007.*
Commission for Performa 07, New York.
Photo by Paula Court.

Christian Jankowski's *Rooftop Routine*
was initially inspired by the artist's Chinese
neighbour Suat Ling Chua, whom he had
surreptitiously observed over several months
hula-hooping regularly on the rooftop of her
building. Learning that Trisha Brown had
in 1973 created a work, *Roof Piece,* stretching
across the rooftops of SoHo, Jankowski
invited two dozen dancers to create a rooftop
routine in homage. To the accompaniment
of a catchy Chinese pop song, which Suat
Ling always listened to on her Walkman
while hula-hooping, Jankowski's neighbour
explains in the subsequent video, edited from
the afternoon's action, how she considered
the exercise both physically and spiritually
uplifting. The parallels with popular fitness
videos are as obvious as the reference to New
York's downtown avant-garde dance of the
1970s, showing Jankowski's ongoing interest
in mixing popular culture and critique of
contemporary art in his work.

KELLY NIPPER
Floyd on the Floor, *2004.*
Commission for Performa 07, Judson Memorial Church, New York.
Photo by Paula Court.

Following the devastation of Hurricane Floyd – a Category 4 storm that swept across the East Coast of the United States in 1999 – Nipper's choreographic investigation of disaster uses prognostication patterns of weather systems and shifts in barometric pressure to direct the movement of eight masked dancers. The performers clutch at an oversized parachute and whirl, tumble, fall and rise, allowing the order of choreographed steps in time to fall under the hazardous and erratic direction of a random system, while simultaneously harnessing it.

JACOLBY SATTERWHITE
Reifying Desire 6, *2012.*
Film still. Commission for the Whitney Biennial 2014, New York.

Satterwhite remixes his performances with home movies, family photos, art-historical images, documentary footage and his mother's drawings in surreal 3D animations that combine to produce a digital portrait. Here he plots individual narratives as data points to be interpreted in the fantasy landscape of a video game universe. Presented as a six-channel video installation, the work scatters attention as real and virtual characters move in and out. The artist becomes an avatar of sorts, into whose world the audience can step.

RAGNAR KJARTANSSON
Bliss, *2011.*
Commission for Performa 11, Abrons Arts Center,
New York.
Photos by Paula Court.

Drawing on the playful, melancholic potential
of repetition in his performance and film, Ragnar
Kjartansson presented *Bliss*, repeating the 2-minute climax
of Mozart's *The Marriage of Figaro* for an uninterrupted
12 hours. The 1786 opera concludes as the Count, after
many egregious missteps, pleads forgiveness from the
Countess and receives it, upon which the royal court
bursts into celebration. Replicating traditional opera
with a full orchestra and trained cast, decadent period
costumes and detailed sets, the performance isolated
only the delirious, intoxicating pinnacle. This epic was
a mesmerizing feat of vocal strength, with audience
members welcome to come and go over the course of its
endless, euphoric repetition.

BRODY CONDON

Case, 2009.
New Museum of Contemporary Art, New York.

Condon's *Case* is a 6-hour rehearsal-like reading of the classic cyberpunk novel *Neuromancer* by William Gibson. The piece is an examination of role-playing, performance and identity, and in particular that of the artist, known for his interest in translating material from popular culture into performance, video and sculpture. Condon combines his rendering of Gibson's 1980s dystopian techno-fetishism with allusions to early 20th-century abstraction, 'virtual reality' and Bauhaus-inspired sculptural props. All are given dramatic accent by the addition of a Gamelan ensemble, a reference to Condon's personal obsessions with transcendence and ritual.

WILLIAM KENTRIDGE
I am not me, the horse is not mine, 2009.
Commission for Performa 09, New York.
Photos by Paula Court.

Part-installation, part-animation and part-theatrical
lecture, *I am not me, the horse is not mine* is a live video
and projection performance in preparation for William
Kentridge's production of Shostakovich's *The Nose* – an
opera based on Gogol's eponymous satire. The story follows
a man who wakes up to discover his nose has separated
from his body and developed a life that surpasses his own.
Kentridge summarizes the tale, which leads him off on
tangents about Soviet Russia, his new production, Gogol's
self-doubt and his own. As his directions begin to split, so
does his body; identical versions of himself, projected via
video, play behind him – the artist excavating both his
process and his layers of interiority.

PHILIPPE PARRENO
How Can We Tell the Dancers From The Dance, *2014.*
Schinkel Pavillon, Berlin.

Since the 1990s, video, sculpture and installation artist Philippe Parreno has upended the notion of art-viewing with his evolving and experiential exhibitions that align the place of the individual viewer in close relation to their parts. Here Parreno merges dance, sculpture and audio in a work that at first appears to be stripped of all objects other than a circular white dance platform at its centre and an octagon of shimmering bright lights in the ceiling above. It is, however, dense with the ghostly presence of live performers. The sound of dancers' footsteps, breathing and jumping – recordings of five Merce Cunningham choreographies (*Duets, RainForest, Roaratorio, Suite for Five,* and *XOVER*) fill the space, while a thick curved wall moves in slow motion around its perimeter, bringing an architectural element into the choreographic conversation.

DOUG AITKEN

Sleepwalkers, 2007.

Installation view. Museum of Modern Art, New York.

Doug Aitken's *Sleepwalkers* is a large-scale film installation that follows five workers – a bicycle messenger, a postal worker, a businessman, an electrician and an office worker – as they awake at night to journey across New York City. Projected onto the Museum of Modern Art's interior facade, eight site-specific films of 13 minutes each show the city as a living, breathing organism fed by the dreams, desires and actions of its inhabitants. The work is experienced by the audience as they circle the museum's interior garden, turning to face each projection. This relationship between viewer and physical exhibition space – an Aitken signature – produces overlapping relationships between the environment and the material of the work itself.

MIKE KELLEY

Extracurricular Activity Projective
Reconstruction #32, 2009.
*Commission for Performa 09, Judson Memorial
Church, New York.*
Photos by Paula Court.

Based on a series of high-school yearbook
photographs depicting extracurricular activities,
Mike Kelley's *Day is Done* is a 2½-hour film where
caricatures and fantastical creatures – vampires,
'goth' kids, mimes and demons – perform in
Kelley's subversive musical-meets-variety-show.
The film was used as a storyboard in reverse
to create the live performance *Extracurricular
Activity*. Using recognizable scenes from the
video – colourful horse heads mounted on
pairs of dancers prance in formation across the
gymnasium; students climb a ladder to pose
for a pyramid class photo – Kelley's spectacle is
an intentionally absurd take on the tropes of
American education, or what he calls 'socially
acceptable rituals of deviance'. With the
detachment of an anthropologist, the artist layers
these diverse references against a backdrop of live
music composed by frequent collaborator Scott
Benzel, spanning rock and roll, heavy metal, film
noir, horror movies, game show themes, bowling
alley tunes and avant-garde noise music.

MAURIZIO CATTELAN
Untitled (Picasso), *1999*.
Museum of Modern Art, New York.

An effigy of Pablo Picasso – an actor wearing
a 1-metre-high (3 ft) mask along with the French
sailor's sweater and sandals favoured by the artist –
mingles among visitors at the Museum of Modern
Art. Featuring Picasso as a European *carnivale* figure,
more often reserved for world leaders, Cattelan
comments on the museum's role in creating art
world icons. 'Picasso' invites passers-by into one of
the most celebrated cultural institutions, where
his place in the canon of art history is maintained.
Cattelan frequently creates miniature stand-ins of
himself, such as the shrunken artist perched on a
high bookshelf in *Mini Me*, 1999, or the boy riding
a remote-controlled tricycle in *Charlie*, 2003, using
them to provocatively critique authority, power,
popular culture and art world pomposity in ways
both comical and profound.

JESPER JUST
True Love is Yet to Come, *2005*.
*Commission for Performa 05, Stephan Weiss
Studios, New York.*

A nostalgic and melancholic exploration of
love and desire, Jesper Just blurs the boundaries
between cinema and stage in a lush combination
of video, hologram and performance. The Danish
artist's first live work explores suffocating male
gender roles and intergenerational romance. For
the nearly 30-minute run, the audience witnesses
a struggle between a sole actor on stage and
figures of men projected around him, ghost-
like and yet shockingly real, as he pursues the
object of his affection, wavering between abject
loneliness, vanity and obsession.

EIJA-LIISA AHTILA
Where is Where? *2008.*
Film still from multi-projection installation.
Museum of Modern Art, New York.

This haunting 55-minute film by Finnish artist Eija-Liisa
Ahtila examines how individual and collective pasts shape lives in
the present. As in much of her filmic work, Ahtila experiments
with weaving two interconnected realities that consider the
consequences of past actions. The first narrative unfolds in
the 1950s during the Algerian war, where two young Arab boys
murder their French friend. The second features two individuals
representing a poet and a hooded figure dressed as death, who
attempt together to understand the boys' actions. Against the
violent backdrop of a wartime massacre, realities and timelines
overlap and give way to each other, relating colonial unrest to
modern conflicts of worldview.

JOAN JONAS
Reading Dante II, *2009.*
Performa 09, The Performing Garage, New York.
Photos by Paula Court.

Since the 1960s, Joan Jonas' arresting poetic performance
and video art has provoked surreal, distorted notions of
perception and corporeality. *Reading Dante II* is an eclectic
video and performance reflection on time, cycle and repetition.
The joyful, scattered storytelling, moving within and beyond
Dante's *Divine Comedy*, is woven together from a collage of
source material: spoken fragments of the epic poem, projected
videos of night time in 1970s New York or Jonas meandering
through the woods of Nova Scotia and a live performance with
collaborator Ragani Haas. The two inhabit the stage in playful,
eccentric vignettes – frantic drawing sessions, a lighthearted
boxing match with thin paper gloves and shadow-play against
the projections – producing a lyrical meditation on the artist's
own dreamy, entrancing purgatory.

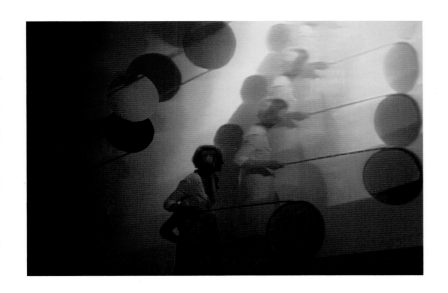

ISAAC JULIEN & RUSSELL MALIPHANT
Cast No Shadow, 2007.
Commission for Performa 07,
Brooklyn Academy of Music, New York.

The extraordinary beauty of visual artist and filmmaker Isaac Julien's works is matched by the intensity of the content that drives him: non-linear narratives exploring cultural and political complexity, shifting tides of economic powers around the globe and neglected histories. For his first evening-length live performance, *Cast No Shadow,* Julien adds two additional films, *Fantôme Afrique* and *Small Boats,* in a remarkable trilogy for the stage that layers dancers in the flesh with their mirrored projections on film, creating a kaleidoscope of choreographed figures and storytelling in time and space. In collaboration with acclaimed British choreographer Russell Maliphant, *Cast No Shadow* uses dramatic geographical landscapes from the North Pole to Burkina Faso and Sicily, as well as bodies in motion, to reveal deeply poignant stories of exploration, exile and loss.

OLAFUR ELIASSON
The Weather Project, 2003.
Tate Modern, London.

In Eliasson's *The Weather Project,* Tate Modern's Turbine Hall was transformed into an artificial sky, representing the transitional time of sunrise or sunset. Lights combine to create a man-made sun that slowly affects the 'weather' in a heavily misted space. The museum becomes a contained environment that harnesses the fleeting and often precarious characteristics that define the natural world, framing and interpreting a simulation of nature in the same way that institutions mediate how art is read and received. While artificial, the mechanisms of sun and environment are revealed to the audience, allowing them to understand their own perception as something constructed.

CHAPTER 2

World Citizenship: Performance as a Global Language

Since the turn of the millennium, with major art centres' increasing interest in work from around the globe, performance art has become a viable medium for reaching across national borders and language barriers. While financial markets are connected through international currency, the 'currency' of artistic output in different geographic locations can be so culturally specific as to have few common threads. As artists working in painting or sculpture may find it difficult to enter the international art conversation from locations further afield of major art institutions, performance-based art has proved itself to be surprisingly accessible across regions and cultures. 'Figurative' in its rendering of a panorama of world cultures, and 'real' in its tendency towards the literal, it stands outside of art theory or institutional critique and distances itself from the 'Western' model. Presented in all manner of contexts, these works also serve to transport audiences back in time and place to the worlds from which the artists came.

KENDELL GEERS
Ritual Resist, *2012.*
La Maison Particulière, Brussels.

Artists from Bangladesh, Pakistan, Afghanistan, Lebanon, China, Egypt, Mexico, Brazil, Russia or South Africa each use performance to articulate complex viewpoints and value systems specific to their countries of birth, where various ethnicities, dialects, gender and class hierarchies converge in a complicated kaleidoscope of culture and social mores. Such multi-tiered references are difficult to contain within a single medium such as painting or sculpture, and even more challenging to communicate with the visceral intensity and proximity to audiences that performance is able to provide. The artists discussed in this chapter each have a strong sense of themselves as citizens operating within a specific world, the parameters of which they delineate from a broad range of cultural choices. Yet theirs is not a form of nationalism – of loyalty to flag or country – but rather an individual, autobiographical identity comprised of many parts. Their symbolic and iconographic references may be recognized and shared easily with others, or they might be a combination of source material and experiences particular to the artist. Either way, citizenship, for many of these artists, has everything to do with fully inhabiting a multiplicity of local beliefs and traditions, while also articulating the conflicts of class and politics that emerge day to day.

This specifically 21st-century notion of citizenship is formed in a world that is increasingly a conglomeration of 'immigrant nations', where constant movement across continents and resettling of populations within other cultures is more extensive in numbers than at any other time in history. The performance material emerging from such ongoing migration forms a tapestry of cultural threads that speaks of ideas beyond art history. Moreover, much of this work is made without consideration of public exhibition in countries that until recently had no gallery system to speak of. Performance, therefore, is a medium of choice for artists working outside the mainstream of the art marketplace. These artists may communicate out of necessity and belief within their immediate communities, yet in doing so are also enable to gain attention in the larger international art world. Presented at biennials and fairs, this vibrant performance material has provided for art world outsiders both a way out and a way in.

In South Africa, over a period of almost three decades since Nelson Mandela was freed from prison in 1990, and became President of South Africa in 1994, performance has functioned in the growing art communities in and around Johannesburg, Cape Town and Durban as a lively and absorbing barometer of the rapidly shifting political landscape. Reacting to half a century of apartheid and the cruel restraints of a police state, William Kentridge has used his expansive talents as draughtsman, performer, playwright, theatre director and visual artist to capture the fraught politics and emotions of the country's recent history. Crediting his theatre training with having provided him with a technique for drawing – the physical precision of one applied to the hand-eye control of the other – Kentridge's work, whether in a gallery or on an opera stage, is an indivisible combination of elements from both theatre and visual art. His animated films, live performances, installations and sculpture are the result of habits and sensibilities that inextricably link the physicality of the live actor with the conceptual underpinnings and visual eloquence of the artist. Other South African artists, such as Athi-Patra Ruga, Nicholas Hlobo, Steven Cohen, Tracey Rose, Kendell Geers, Kemang Wa Lehulere, Nandipha Mntambo, Hasan and Husain Essop, Zanele Muholi, Robin Rhode, Nelisiwe Xaba, Basil Jones and Adrian Kohler of Handspring Puppet Company, similarly use live performance as a critical tool to make their way through the maze of eleven official languages and the innumerable customs and traditions of South Africa, producing live performance alongside or in combination with a range of other media, including photography, drawing, painting, tapestry and sculpture.

In the vast subcontinent of India, international art centres have since 2000 emerged in Delhi and Mumbai, as well as in Kerala and neighbouring Dhaka, Bangladesh. Fuelled by rapid macroeconomic growth, India's 'decade of development' produced a burgeoning interest in contemporary art as new galleries, art fairs and alternative spaces opened doors for a new generation of artists attuned to the critical and intellectual discourse that came with it. For them, creating art that both retained its cultural significance on home ground yet had the possibility of finding a place in global art history was an important goal. Given an easy familiarity with ceremonial public spectacle and live performance of all kind –

←
SUBODH GUPTA
Spirit Eaters, *2012.*
For KHOJLive 12. New Delhi.
Photo by Satya Rai Nagpaul.

so integral to South Asian culture – including music and classical Indian dance, temple feasts and religious celebrations, many younger artists consider performance a comfortable extension of their art-making in other media. Artist Nikhil Chopra translates some of the exuberant aesthetic of India's festivals and pageantry into elegant costumed performances that often take place over several days in a gallery or outdoors, and which incorporate drawings and elaborate installations. The Raqs Media Collective, formed in 1992 by Jeebesh Bagchi, Monica Narula and Shuddhabrata Sengupta frequently curate exhibitions that take the form of lecture-demonstrations on culture and political thought, involving text and projections, actors and occasionally a drummer or singer. Subodh Gupta, based in Delhi, has created monumental sculptures out of everyday utensils found in the Indian kitchen, and produced related performances that serve as both social commentary and celebration of community, while performances by Nalini Malani, Pushpamala N., Atul Bhalla, Shilpa Gupta and Mahbubur Rahman add detail and nuance to understanding the complexities of contemporary Indian art and politics.

The Chinese art world opened to Western influence in the mid 1980s – an exhibition by Robert Rauschenberg in

↑
ELENA KOVYLINA
Would You Like a Cup of Coffee? *2010.*
Garage Museum of Contemporary Art,
Moscow.
Photo by Artem Zhitenev.

NIKHIL CHOPRA
Young Raj Chitrakar: Memory Drawing X, *2010.*
Chatterjee & Lal, Mumbai.
Photo by Shivani Gupta.

Beijing in 1985 receiving record numbers of visitors – while within China performance by artists as a public medium for questioning 'official' art in a shifting political and social landscape had been gathering momentum for more than a decade. Highly experimental, and considered a necessary means for questioning the nature of art as well as the artist's role in society, a series of performances were planned as part of the polemical 'China Avant-Garde' exhibition that opened in February 1989. One of the first institutionally sanctioned exhibitions where performance was integral to the curatorial overview, this acceptance was short-lived when Xiao Lu notoriously fired two shots from a handgun into her installation, shutting down the exhibition, which had been open for just a few hours, and reinforcing the perception of 'performance art' as a subversive and publicly disruptive platform. A few months later, student protests would be violently quelled in Tiananmen Square and art, as with all aspects of Chinese society, would be more highly regulated and censored than ever before. Even so, artists in cities from Shanghai to Beijing, Guangzhou, Chengdu, Harbin, Lijiang and Shenzhen continued to stage events, frequently out of public view. In the 1990s, these staged performances, in small studios in Beijing's East Village or in the countryside, that were documented and later exhibited as elegant, highly composed large-scale photographs, would go to make up the travelling exhibitions such as 'Translated Acts', 2002, and 'Between Past and Future', 2004, seen in the United States and in Europe. Considered 'not performance' and therefore less threatening than the live art that they depicted, powerful images by Zhang Huan, Song Dong, Feng Mengbo, Qiu Zhijie and Xu Zhen, among many others, constituted the first wave of significant art coming out of the 'new' China.

In Russia, the decades following the break up of the Soviet Union in 1991 saw artists emerging from a long period of invisibility, where performance had functioned as a form of silent resistance. With no public outlets for their work – no galleries, art magazines, museum exhibitions or media coverage

– and working under a cloud of constant surveillance, artists in the 1970s and '80s had devised strategies that included clandestine performances and exhibitions in their apartments, referred to as 'APTART'. The 1990s saw artists building on these earlier collective actions, while performance in the first decade of the new millennium reflected the daily fluctuations of political change across the fifteen republics that made up the former Soviet Union. Mocking the instability of political and social institutions as well as the ostentatious wealth of the new capitalists, some artists used absurdist humour to point to the public's underlying frustration. Alexander Brener, The Voina Group, and the Blue Noses (Alexander Shaburov and Vyacheslav Mizin) mixed agit-prop stunts on the street, frequently designed to gain maximum media attention. Others, such as Elena Kovylina and Andrey Kuzkin, mined the psychological implications of constantly shifting social values. Their work raised questions of feminism, gender politics or religion – subjects rarely aired in public – and responded with metaphorically rich events that described their own existential distress. Kovylina danced with random strangers selected from a crowd, downing shots of vodka after each dance until she collapsed from exhaustion and drunkenness in *Waltz*, 2001. She also set up a tea party on the street with chairs pulled up around an elaborately set table, only to set it on fire, in *Voulez-vous un café? ou Feu le monde bourgeois*, 2009. In *Walking in Circles*, 2008, Kuzkin spent 4½ hours walking in a circle that the artist described as 'an act of solidarity with people who are forced to carry on their shoulders the hardness of everyday life which is so unbearably difficult in this country'.

Argentinian artist Amalia Pica draws on her country's long history of censorship and intellectual suppression, the effects of which impacted her childhood (she was born in 1978). Under the fascist military dictatorship of the 1970s, the teaching of Venn diagrams to schoolchildren was forbidden on the basis that the concept of 'overlap' might encourage collaboration and dissent. Using the brightly coloured geometric objects of the Venn system, Pica created live 'intersections', where performers and the public spontaneously arranged hand-held triangles and circles, suggesting revolutionary possibilities through simple acts of sharing and communal art-making. For Mexico City-based Rafael Lozano-Hemmer, the unprovoked horrors of the Tlatelolco student massacre of 1968 were recalled four decades later, using a megaphone planted at the site. Passers-by were encouraged to stop and speak their painful memories into the mouthpiece. Describing the oppression and torture of an earlier time, their voices were broadcast to those gathered in the public square, while the loudspeakers also connected to powerful light projectors that criss-crossed the night's sky, following the rhythms of their spoken words.

Though responding to political turmoil, much of this work is not overtly political. Such art actions are in themselves radical departures from conventional painting or sculpture, and it was in the period from the 1960s through the 1980s, during serial juntas in countries on the South American axis, that a deep connection to performance prevailed. Building on the work of Neo-Concretists in Brazil, such as Lygia Clark, Hélio Oiticica, and Lygia Pape, the generation that followed showed a deep sensitivity to the ways in which objects and performance are connected, both visually and viscerally, as extensions of the body. For these artists, making art involved finding a natural balance between objects and bodies in space.

For many artists living and working outside of the limited European modernist traditions, making art is a part of life. Its ceremonies and rituals, power systems and linguistic histories provide rich sources that the artists are entirely comfortable mining for their own creativity. Furthermore, the physical experience of growing up in geographically and culturally distinctive settings translates into movement and music, clothing and adornment, storytelling and vocalization in ways that can themselves be infinitely performative. Bold and highly visual, close-up and personal, performance speaks of deeply human concerns, and does so with a level of experimentation that can keep the viewer enthralled, watchful and surprised.

TANIA BRUGUERA
Tatlin's Whisper #5, 2008.
Tate Modern, London.

Bruguera's work explores the spaces between
government oppression, censorship, and political compromise.
In *Tatlin's Whisper*, she specifically investigates the tactics
used by those in power to manipulate and overwhelm the
public. Two mounted policemen manoeuvre through Tate
Modern's Turbine Hall performing crowd control, corralling,
and separating spectators. Incongruously applied to a gallery-
going audience, the mechanisms of authority are shown
close up, implying the nascent violence in tightly managed
political regimes.

NANDIPHA MNTAMBO
Inkunzi Emnyama, *2009.*
Stevenson Gallery, Cape Town and Johannesburg.

South African artist Nandipha Mntambo uses
animal hides, particularly cow, to transform herself in
performative video and photographic works that reframe
treatments of colonial and postcolonial femininities. Named
for the Xhosa term meaning 'black bull', *Inkunzi Emnyama* is
a photographic work in which Mntambo bows in repetition
of the final gestures of a bullfight, performed moments before
the act of killing. Outfitted in the costume of a toreador,
and with a cow hide wrapped around her waist as formal
tails, Mntambo is both hunter and hunted, cow and bull,
man and woman, revelling in the machismo of the male-
dominated Spanish sport.

MING WONG
Whodunnit? *2004.*
Film stills.

Inserting himself into Western film
history by re-staging iconic cinematic scenes,
Ming Wong uses the classic Agatha Christie
play, *The Mousetrap* (considered the longest-
running English language play), to turn a
murder mystery into a political detective
story about identity. Wong's amateur actors
are selected according to descriptions of
ethnic categories outlined in diversity
requirements for funding from Arts Council
England (African, Afro-Caribbean, Asian,
Chinese, Middle Eastern, Latin American,
Greek Cypriot, Eastern European, Jewish
and Irish). They perform their soap opera
in heavy but shifting accents on a multi-
cultural battleground alongside a comic
police detective and, rather than solving a
traditional 'whodunnit?', raise the separate
question of the identity of the individual.

DORA GARCÍA
Die Klau Mich Show, *2013.*
Commission for Documenta 13, Kassel.
Photo by Lauren Huret.

Inspired by the 1968 book *Klau Mich* (Steal Me) by German radicals Rainer Langhans and Fritz Teufel, which dealt with anti-authoritarian political dissent, Spanish artist Dora García staged a weekly TV talk-show for visitors to Documenta 13. García frequently draws on interactivity and performance in a gallery setting to force the relationship between artwork, audience and place. In this extended 'theatre rehearsal', participants included the original writers of *Steal Me*, the Art & Language group, playwright-curator Felix Ensslin and members of the German Pirate Party. García's performance-as-public-access-television, broadcast locally, gave licence to the programmers to revisit extreme political ideologies of the 1960s without the scrutiny of authorities.

RAQS MEDIA COLLECTIVE
Seen at Secunderabagh, *2013*.
Commission for Documenta 13, Kassel.

    Known for their experimental documentaries interrogating
contemporary India and its political and psychological histories,
the Delhi-based trio Raqs Media Collective collaborated with
theatre director Zuleikha Chaudhuri on *Seen at Secunderabagh* – a
performance and installation that portrays the purposeful distortion
of a historical document. A 19th-century Felice Beato photograph
depicts four men and a white horse standing in the ruins of a
destroyed, neoclassical building, piles of rubble and bones scattered
around them. Taken months after a violent rebellion against the
British East India Company, the scene was staged, as the bones from
previous deaths dug up and arranged. Through a series of frantic,
repetitive motions and utterances, the performers respond to the
image – its manipulation, the reality of violence and colonialism
around it and the complexities of conveying truth through medium.

PUSHPAMALA N. AND CLARE ARNI

Our Lady of Velankanni, *2003.*
C-print on metallic paper, 56 x 37 cm
(22 x 14⅓ in.).
Bangalore.

South Indian artist Pushpamala N. and
British photographer Clare Arni explore
photography's complicated history as a tool
of ethnographic documentation and identity-
building. Together, the artists construct
scenes and serve as protagonists in a series of
performance photographs that recreate South
Indian female archetypes from across the region's
iconic art history and visual culture. They play
with extremes of reality and fiction, subject and
object, photographer and photographed. The
scenes include reconstructions of a 16th-century
yogini, or female yogi, from a painted miniature,
a newspaper print of two thieves holding
identity plates and a film still of a Bollywood
starlet from the cover of a 1960s issue of *India
Today.* This photograph, *Our Lady of Velankanni,*
depicts Pushpamala as the Marian icon, believed
to have first appeared in the 16th century in
the Indian town of Velankanni. The worship
of the Velankanni Mary melds Eastern and
Western belief, tradition and aesthetics.

LIU BOLIN
Hiding in New York No. 8 – Cereal, *2013*.
Photograph, 149.8 x 112.4 cm (59 x 44¼ in.).
Klein Sun Gallery, New York.

Chinese artist Liu Bolin camouflages himself with the bright
colours of excess and consumerism, painting his body to disappear
perfectly against the backdrop of grocery, convenience or toy store
aisles. Allowing his surroundings – from lush scenes of stacked
magazines, rows of soda cans, or piles of produce – to swallow him
whole, the practice of hiding in plain sight spans the last ten years of his
career. *Hiding in New York No. 8 – Cereal* depicts the artist in front of rows
of cereal boxes all neatly placed along the shelves of an aisle, complete
with logos, slogans and mascots. The work communicates an anxiety
in the wake of China's rapid economic boom, and the way in which
individuals have become subsumed within a newly globalized present.

GOLDIN + SENNEBY

RIGHT The Decapitation of Money, *2010.*
Photo by Aurélien Mole.
RIGHT BELOW The Decapitation of
Money, Walk in Marly Forest with
Angus Cameron, *2010.*
Photo by Emilie Villez.

Swedish duo Simon Goldin and
Jakob Senneby, known for borrowing
methods from the financial sector to
create conceptual videos, workshops
and performances, devised a two-part
installation that charts the evolution of
currency from the 18th century to today.
The transformation of money from physical
capital into abstracted value is explored
in a walking tour of the Marly forest near
Versailles, led by geographer and economist
Angus Cameron, followed by a gallery
exhibition. The tour includes reference to
Georges Bataille's secret society, who met
in the same area in the 1940s to celebrate
the murder of King Louis XVI. The stylized
installations include a reception area with
chairs and a desk, featuring Bataille's 1949
essay 'La Part Maudite' on economies of
excess. In an adjacent space, the artists
project a video lecture, explaining the
significance of Bataille's essay and its
connection to the origins of the Eurodollar.

HASAN AND HUSAIN ESSOP

Fast Food, 2008.
C-print on Fuji Crystal archive paper, 123 x 70 cm
(48½ x 27½ in.).
Goodman Gallery, Cape Town.

For South African twins Hasan and Husain Essop, the performance and photographing of the daily rituals of young Muslim men in an ethnically and racially diverse Cape Town combine to form striking images that are both secular and devout. In *Fast Food*, pop culture meets religious devotion as a group of men gather for sunset prayer on a Cape beach to break their Ramadan fast with McDonalds burgers and fries. The wordplay on 'fast' further underlines the overlapping worlds of religious ceremony and consumer convenience, providing a highly contemporary window into traditional observances that coexist in the same territory as our throwaway culture.

HARRELL FLETCHER & ERIC STEEN
A Walk to Pikes Peak, *2012*.
Colorado Springs.

Democratizing the role of the artist through his socially
engaging, publicly collaborative installations and projects,
Harrell Fletcher organized *A Walk to Pikes Peak,* a hike that
investigated and expanded a community's understanding of its
local environment. Over the course of three days participants
trekked from Colorado Springs to Pikes Peak, a 4,300-metre-
high (14,115 ft) summit in the Rocky Mountains. Preparing a
short lesson on the area – whether an oral history, personal
memory or scientific presentation – each participant becomes
an artist, educator and student, considering the geography
not only as land but as a deeply personal, constantly evolving
marker for the individuals who experience it.

SHILPA GUPTA
Don't See Don't Hear Don't Speak, 2009.
Public installation for Atti Democratici, Bolzano.

Playing with the principle of non-violence to 'see no evil, hear no evil, speak no evil' popularized by Mahatma Gandhi, Mumbai-based Shilpa Gupta's *Don't See Don't Hear Don't Speak* consists of large-scale photographs of Indian youths, standing single-file or in rows, each extending their arms and covering the eyes, ears or mouth of their neighbour. The communal, policed action she invokes turns Gandhi's original on its head. Rather than keeping the mind and body pure from bad thoughts or actions, these gestures leave the subjects of Gupta's photos inhibited and uninformed.

MAHBUBUR RAHMAN
Transformation, 2005.
Bangladesh.

Bangladeshi artist Mahbubur Rahman's *Transformation* takes inspiration from the writings of poet Syed Shamus Haq. In Haq's story, an indigo farmer in Bangladesh rebels against British colonizers who retaliate and strip him of his every belonging, leaving him destitute and forcing him to use his own body to plough the fields in place of his buffalos. Donning a horned headdress and a mask made of jute, Rahman's suffocating costume transforms him into a beast of labour. He moves, swims and lumbers, barely able to see, and struggles as the protagonist of the story struggled, and as so many in India continue to suffer the social and economic consequences of a colonial past.

ELENA KOVYLINA
Would You Like a Cup of Coffee? *2010.*
Garage Museum of Contemporary Art, Moscow.
Photo by Artem Zhitenev.

Elena Kovylina's *Would You Like a Cup of Coffee?* or *Burn the World of the Bourgeois!* takes the form of a radical tea party, where the artist adopts the role of aggressive social critic in a performance that harkens to past and present political dissent in Russia. Kovylina invites her audience to partake of tea and treats as she recites political statements against the bourgeoisie, all the while clad in high fashion regalia. During the course of the tea, in an unexpected moment, she sets the tablecloth on fire, destroying the classed ritual and its artefacts in an ironic moment of protest.

↑
AMALIA PICA
A∩B∩C, *2013.*
Museo Tamayo, Mexico City.
Photo by Daniela Uribe.

←
ATHI-PATRA RUGA
Ilulwane, *2011.*
Commission for Performa 11 with the Museum
for African Art. Performed again in Cape Town.

With his surreal, technicolour performances, costuming and fabrication, South African artist Athi-Patra Ruga presents subversive, often camp, imaginings of the physical body and of cross-cultural identities. *Ilulwane*, performed in a cavernous, red-lit gymnasium pool, is a haunting, synchronized swimming ceremony. A dozen women move in dark water as a suspended figure, obscured of race or gender by a large white cape, dangles above them. With video projections inspired by Alvin Baltrop's iconic 1970s photographs of New York's gay pier culture, and collaborating with South African musician Spoek Mathambo on audio compositions, Ruga's performance presented an intimate ritual of water and time, speaking to both his Xhosa heritage and the AIDS epidemic.

Argentinian artist Amalia Pica draws on her country's history of censorship and intellectual suppression, where under the military dictatorship of the 1970s and '80s the teaching of intersection, and even its mathematical representation in the form of overlapping lines or shapes, was prohibited as it might encourage collaboration and dissent. Her piece *A ∩B ∩C*, reads as 'A intersects B intersects C'. Dancers manipulate a series of brightly coloured transparent shapes made of acrylic, moving, arranging and overlaying them into spontaneous formations and designs, allowing them to show through each other, and creating un-choreographed patterns. The revolutionary possibilities of intersection are elaborated, as a community of performers collaborate to create something new.

NIKHIL CHOPRA

Yog Raj Chitrakar: Memory
Drawing IX, *2009.*
Commission for Performa 09 with
New Museum, New York.
Photo by Tina Lange.

This five-day performance as a character
inspired by the Delhi-based artist's plein-
air-painting grandfather saw him travel
each day to Ellis Island, gateway for millions
of immigrants for sixty years, wearing full
Victorian costume. There, he produces
enormous charcoal drawings of Manhattan.
Transforming the New Museum lobby into
a 1920s bedchamber, he hangs the drawings
each night and performs domestic rituals in
an anachronistic investigation of evolution,
voyeurism and perception in urban life.

CARLOS AMORALES

Spider Galaxy, *2007.*
Commission for Performa 07, The Atrium,
New York.
Photo by Paula Court.

Mexico City-based Amorales' *Spider Galaxy*
brings together a haunting sculptural installation
and performance, where four hundred wooden
blocks serve as the stage for a lone dancer dressed
in a carapace resembling reptile, robot, insect and
bird. Representing the negative space in a spider's
web, the raised platform constitutes both stage and
seating, coming to life as a subsonic composition
reverberates upwards from the wood to be heard
and felt. Evoking associations of the spider's web
with trap, home and icon of the horror film, the
slow and measured gestures of the dancer explore
the physical properties of the stage and her costume.
She walks along the diagonals of the octagon, subtly
manipulating the carapace's cocoon-like shape in a
constant transformation.

CHTO DELAT
Perestroika Songspiel, *2008.*
Poster for play.

Operating through visual performance and organized
actions, and using posters and publications to promote leftist
cultural, economic and social positions, St Petersburg-based
collective Chto Delat (What is to be done?), in collaboration
with sound collective Ultra-Red, developed a play that
explored the contentious social dynamics of community
housing. Using the methodology of Bertolt Brecht's didactic
'learning plays', based on 48-hour seminars and workshops,
the resulting performance, staged amid towering black crates,
followed the trials of a community centre's formation, the
varied beliefs of its participants, and the complex politics of
the social space they must share.

RAFAEL LOZANO-HEMMER
Voz Alta, 2008.
Mexico City.

Voz Alta ('spoken out loud') was a memorial commemorating
the 40th anniversary of the 1968 student massacre in Mexico City.
Set in the public square where the massacre took place, survivors,
poets, activists, musicians, politicians and the friends and families
of those lost – altogether numbering in the thousands – take turns
speaking into a megaphone connected to a series of four search
lights. These point to local landmarks and government buildings,
including the Ministry of Foreign Affairs and the Monument to
the Revolution. The lights beam silently in time with the speakers'
voices, brightening and dimming according to the amplification
and intonation of their speech. Broadcast to a local radio station,
the project made public the stories of these participants, a phantom
voice over Mexico City that reminded its inhabitants of those lost.

BEATRIZ SANTIAGO MUÑOZ
A. Listens, *2004.*
Gasworks, London.

This 7-minute video by Puerto Rican artist Beatriz
Santiago Muñoz introduces the viewer to Anne, a young
Londoner and agoraphobe who describes her superhuman
hearing. Unfolding an exercise of language and narrative,
the video leads Anne's dialogue with a number of questions:
What kind of sounds can you pick up? How far away can you
hear conversations? What is your range? Anne answers, at times
truthfully and at times not, the veracity of her statements at
any given moment remaining unclear. Working with a non-
actor, as she does across her works, Muñoz is attracted to the
authenticity of such performances, where she encourages her
protagonists to reveal truth through fiction.

THEASTER GATES
Stony Island Arts Bank, *2012 onwards.*
Chicago.
Photo by Tom Harris.

Theaster Gates combines the machinations of city
government and housing authorities with art world economics
to reanimate and transform blocks of neglected houses and
storefronts on the South Side of Chicago. Working with local
communities, Gates established the Stony Island Trust & Savings
Bank Building, abandoned for decades, as an expansive cultural
hub, with a library, movie house and facilities for performances,
meetings and workshops. From large-scale urban development
projects to intimate theatre performances, his works join powerful
social activism with the artist's talents as singer, poet, playwright
and performer. Together, these elements combine into a powerful
and rigorous aesthetic whole.

TUNGA

Afinidades Eletivas, 2004.

Installation view. Galeria Millan, São Paulo.

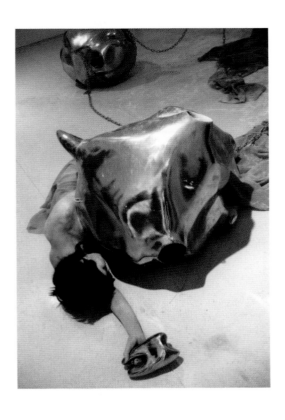

Channelling alchemy through surrealist forms and assemblages, video and sculpture, Brazilian artist Tunga creates trance-like, ceremonial performances within gauzy, unsettling tableaus, emphasizing the creative continuity among forms, in line with a generation of fellow Brazilian artists whose work extends the limits of the body. Here giant walking canes, oversized aluminium teeth and long silk fabrics attached to clamps hang from the ceiling, forming a transparent shelter filled with dripping chains and bulbous sculptures and implying a continuum – a single body, derived from a common generation – 'of teeth growing in one mouth'. On several occasions, the installation was activated by four women, naked and smeared with the floor's chalky powder, moving through the space.

WAEL SHAWKY

Dictums 10:120, 2011–13.

Commission for Sharjah Biennial 11.

Shawky straddles religious histories and complex, cross-cultural narratives, and here subverts Qawwali – a lively, devotional Sufi music form – in a biting institutional critique of the language around contemporary art. Performing at the Sharjah Biennial, thirty-two men sit in a Sharjah alley, chanting, clapping and filling the space with sound indecipherable to non-Urdu speakers. Rather than using traditional spiritual lyrics, the performance translates disparate fragments of talks held at the Biennial, producing a disorienting chant to mirror the often alienating, oblique language of contemporary art discourse.

SUN YUAN & PENG YU
Dogs That Cannot Touch Each Other, *2003.*
Today Art Museum, Beijing.

Dogs That Cannot Touch Each Other was a deeply disturbing and rightfully controversial live installation involving eight pit bulls trapped in cage-like mechanical treadmills. Paired to face each other, inches apart, in ferocious attack mode, this cruel event was for the artists a symbolic reference to the repression experienced and expressed by many Chinese artists of the period. More recently video documentation of this work sparked considerable public objection for its abuse of animals.

HONG-KAI WANG
Music While We Work, *2011.*
Film stills. Commission for Venice Biennale.

Taiwanese artist Hong-Kai Wang's
Music While We Work is a semi-biographic
inquest into the power of sound in building
and preserving identity, memory and social
relationships. The artist invited five retired
sugar factory workers and their wives to
return to the century-old plant in Huwei,
Taiwan, once a hub of sugar production where
the men had formerly worked. Trained by a
composer in using microphones and recording
devices, the couples move across the space,
documenting the industrial noises of the
factory and its surroundings, and noting their
reactions and observations to the sounds
and settings. The participants unmask a
language of memory within familiar sounds,
tracing their origins and functions. Presented
as a video installation, the piece serves as a
memorial to itself, the place, its history and
the former lives of these individuals.

ATUL BHALLA
Pharta Kuan, 2005.
Archival pigment print, 33 x 25 cm (13 x 10 in.). Partapur, Rajasthan.

New Delhi-based Atul Bhalla plays with local lore in *Pharta Kuan*,
a project set in the small Indian village of Bori, its name meaning
'sack'. Previously known as Pharta Kuan (translated as 'wherever
well' for the many wells in the area), the village was, according to
legend, renamed Bori by a local king, who received a bounty of grain
sacks from the village in lieu of tax payments. In this ritualistic
performance and photographic series, Bhalla retrieves the town's
original name to focus on the importance of water. Photographs of
all 93 of its functioning wells feature specially cast buckets and mugs
made from local sand alongside each water source, serving as both
a reminder of local history and the spiritual, physical and political
significance of water conservation in India and globally.

MAREPE
Vermelho-Amarelo-Azul-Verde, *2005*.
Centre Pompidou, Paris.
Photo by Bertrand Prevost.

Known for playful sculptures that merge readymade tradition
with the commonplace found objects of his native Brazil, Marepe
here stages a dynamic, luminous performance at the Centre
Pompidou. Two dancers wear enormous, jewel-hued sacks filled with
multicoloured balloons: red for humanity, yellow for electricity, blue
for air and green for water. Gliding through the space and colliding
into each other, the dancers transform their shimmering gowns as
dozens of balloons soar and shift inside the fabric. With each chaotic,
joyous motion the balloons create new, transient sculptural forms,
evolving until the last balloon has popped.

JEREMY DELLER
The Battle of Orgreave (an injury to one is an injury to all), *2001.*
Film stills. Orgreave, South Yorkshire.

Jeremy Deller examines collective memory in British political histories across video, installation and collaborative performance. *The Battle of Orgreave*, a day-long performance, saw the re-enactment of the violent 1984 confrontation between workers and police at the Orgreave coking plant. Having watched the dispute on television as a child, two decades later he assembles a massive cast of approximately eight hundred historical re-enactors and two hundred ex-miners and police who were present at the event. Participants perform the brutal scenes, in which riot-geared police chase strikers through an idyllic landscape, eulogizing and honouring the event and acknowledging both this significant moment in Britain's labour history and its lingering impact on citizens.

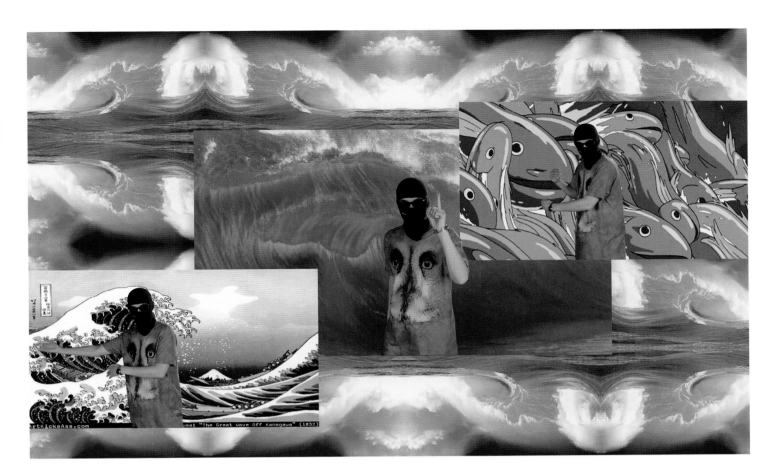

HITO STEYERL
Liquidity Inc., 2014.
Installation view. Artists Space, New York.

Producing satirical, politically-engaged video installations, Hito Steyerl investigates the speed and proliferation of new digital media. *Liquidity Inc.*, a dense experience of virtual distraction and economic uncertainty, has viewers melt into amorphous blue beanbags at the end of a sloping ramp, absorbed by the enormous screen before them. A narrative forms of Jacob Wood – a financier who, after losing his job in the 2008 recession, turns his Mixed Martial Arts hobby into a career. There are endless interruptions to this unfolding: waves, sound clips, a balaclava-clad girl making ominous weather announcements. Investigating the instability of the 21st century, the video emphasizes the necessity of liquidity – of funds, skills, identity – for survival in the contemporary era.

SUBODH GUPTA
Spirit Eaters, *2013.*
Film still. New Delhi.

Exploring commonplace domestic objects, communal
traditions and the rituals of food and consumption in India,
multimedia artist Subodh Gupta produced *Spirit Eaters,* a
performance that isolates cultural grief through a scene of
ceremonial eating. Three *kanthababas* – individuals paid by
mourning families to eat excessively on behalf of the deceased
– sit cross-legged beside each other, in front of them plates
of a thick, white, rice-based substance. They gorge on the
food barehanded, devouring as they talk among themselves,
all the while watched by an audience of strangers. Without
a cause of grief the intimate act is seen for its mesmerizing,
gluttonous motions – a culturally-specific tableau removed
from its geography and cultural reference.

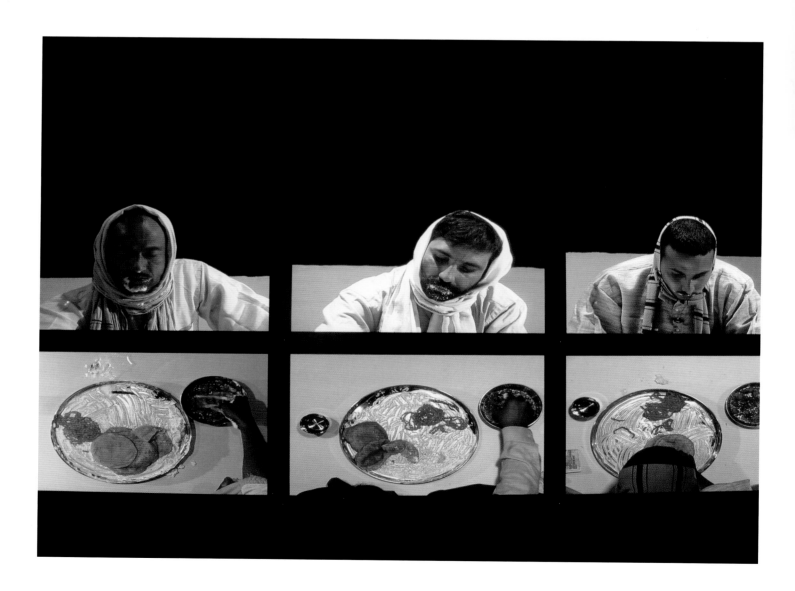

ZHU MING

14 O'clock, July 27th, 2008.
Sichuan.

Zhu Ming has performed his bubble series in sites
both urban and remote, including the Sydney Harbour in
Australia and the remote mountains of China. *14 O'clock,
July 27th* is a continuation of the series, in which over a
dozen individuals occupy an enormous clear bubble
perched in the fog-covered high altitudes of Sichuan.
Geographically removed from artificial influence or any
semblance of civilization, the mesmerizing orb is foreign
to its surroundings. The individuals within it, naked as
they rest, create an unobtrusive communal space, also a
metaphor for suffocation and isolation. This presentation
of Ming's work as photography reflects a period in Chinese
history when performance was considered highly subversive
and prohibited by the authorities.

ARAYA RASDJARMREARNSOOK
Two Planets: Manet's *Le Déjeuner sur l'herbe* and
Thai Farmers, *2008.*
Film still. Thailand.

Thai artist Araya Rasdjarmrearnsook's videos, photographs and
performances frequently invoke the Buddhist saying that life begins
and ends in the village. This performative video begins with a group
of Thai villagers, young and old, seated in front of Manet's famous
painting, the pastoral settings mirroring each other and establishing
a connection across time and place between mid-19th-century France
and modern day Thailand. The different modes of reception and
interpretation offered by the farmers' conversation show an alternative
way of looking at art in terms of the subjects' daily concerns.

RIRKRIT TIRAVANIJA
The Land, *1998 onwards*.
Farm and art space, Sanpatong.

The Land Foundation is a working farm in
a village near the city of Chiang Mai, Thailand,
that unites art, design and advocacy, engaging
artists and local farmers in the region. Meant
as an exercise in community-building, discourse
and social engagement, the project has brought
together local and international artists –
among them Philippe Parreno, Danish collective
SUPERFLEX and François Roche – who have
made contributions involving housing, energy
and community in cultivating new modes of
artistic expression. The Land has provided
valuable resources to artists and farmers, and
created a grassroots social platform in the area
where local government has been unable to help.

KENDELL GEERS
Ritual Resist, *2012*.
La Maison Particulière, Brussels.

A naked man and woman lean against the large mirror between them, supported by their body weight. Neither sees the other, but each stares at their own reflection. As they move across the gallery space, pressing into the mirror and each other, limbs and body parts give way to fatigue, sweat loosens the ability to keep the object aloft, and balance wavers in a compromised and precarious action where failure is a constant possibility. Hovering on the edge between what looks like dance and martial art, as the pair move in tandem, sometimes violently, to keep the mirror from falling, the anxiety of exertion is felt by the audience as well. For South African born artist, Kendell Geers, a longstanding interest in the spectatorship of impending disaster is both metaphorically and viscerally represented in this aesthetically charged work.

NICHOLAS HLOBO
Ungamqhawuli, 2008.
Michael Stevenson Gallery, Cape Town.

Hlobo's poetic and layered paintings, installations and performances begin with ruminations on the Xhosa titles that he uses to establish mood and meaning. *Ungamqhawuli* translates as 'to cut off' or 'to interrupt', but is also a suggestion that 'all hell will break loose', as 'when kids are playing too wildly and the swing snaps'. Strapped into a cot and using a pulley to lift himself off the floor into the air, Hlobo lies still, and sometimes falls asleep. Always the storyteller, this tale is nestled inside another: the overall title of the exhibition in the midst of which the performance took place, '*Kwatsityw'iziko*', means 'crossing the hearth', referring most literally to sex, and to the practice of being quiet to avoid being heard by others in the act. The suspended figure can be seen as a grown-up child or as an adult longing to be a well-behaved child again.

ZHANG HUAN
Buddhist Relics, *2003.*
DiverseWorks, Houston.

Known for his visceral, occasionally masochistic
performances, multimedia artist Zhang Huan merges social
intervention, ritual and Buddhist philosophy. In *Buddhist Relics*
he presented a dramatized, politically critical ceremony of
the ancient Chinese cupping practice. Perched atop a tiered,
mountainous gown and surrounded by miniature pagodas,
the artist suctions glass cups to his naked body, performing a
treatment used to release bad qì energy in Chinese medicine.
Pigeons are attached to each cup by string, alluding to
the zoonotic respiratory virus SARS that spread through
China in the early 2000s. In an act of prayer and mourning
alongside the pagodas – which house the ashes of enlightened
monks – Huan staged a meditation on the disease, and the
government's infamously negligent response to its impact.

SANFORD BIGGERS
THE SOMETHIN' SUITE, 2007.
Commission for Performa 07, The Box, New York.
Photo by Paula Court.

Complicating traditional cultural narratives, Sanford Biggers' *THE SOMETHIN' SUITE* was a psychologically disorienting, cross-cultural variety show, gesturing towards racialized minstrel traditions. Imani Uzuri, a black woman in whiteface, sang a distorted, unsettling interpretation of *Strange Fruit*, Billie Holiday's haunting lament on racial lynching, as a video of black men scaling trees played behind her. Other cast members including Saul Williams and Martin Luther, dressed in both contemporary costumes and those of the Old South, sang, rapped and performed spoken word in a multi-faceted performance that interrogated the formation of stereotypes and confronted the implications and legacy of blackface in music, culture and industry.

C H A
P T E R
3

Radical Action:
on Performance and Politics

COCO FUSCO
A Room of One's Own: Women and
Power in the New America, *2006–08.*
Work in progress first shown at Performa 05,
The Kitchen, New York.
Photo by Paula Court.

A s migration across national borders began to accelerate in the first decade
of the 21st century, altering the cultural landscape of many societies that
had previously been majority-based, further disruption has been caused
by a roiling series of wars in Eastern Europe and the Middle East as well
as North and Central Africa. The terrorist attacks of September 11, 2001
and the so-called 'war on terror' that they unleashed escalated general
unease across urban populations worldwide. The United States Patriot
Act of October that year gave American law enforcement agencies carte
blanche to gather intelligence, hold and detain civilians and watch over
their daily lives with surveillance cameras, bugging devices and any other
means necessary. As talk of a United States attack on Iraq in the early
2000s was fuelled by imagined weapons of mass destruction, protesters
gathered to stop the warmongering. February 2003 witnessed the largest
mass-mobilization of more than sixty million people in six hundred
nations to protest against, and hopefully halt, an impending war. It was
not to be. One month later American bombs fell on Baghdad.

The capture of Saddam Hussein in 2003 and his execution three years later, the tumbling of heads of state in adjacent regions and the continued occupation of Afghanistan by American forces precipitated violent shifts in the political landscape and further intensified sectarian schisms throughout the Middle East. The 'theatre of war' was streamed into living rooms in London, Paris, Berlin and New York, as well as into those countries where soldiers and insurgents were most actively in battle. With daily assaults depicted in news media in unrelenting detail, and as social media became ubiquitous by the decade's end, the general public took to the streets, phones held high, to record civil wars as they occurred in real time. Crowdsourcing became a tool of the endless days and nights of occupation, with songs and poetry identifying each location and each cause. The phenomenon of these protest movements was followed as much by political observers on the ground as by cultural critics in the ether of social media. The Green Movement, the Arab Spring, the Occupy movement, Pussy Riot, Taksim Square and Black Lives Matter have been less about mounting the barricades of old and more about asserting public ownership of urban space, whether in Cairo, Istanbul or Baltimore, claiming the city centre as the people's 'agora' – a place of power symbolizing the civic and the common good. These movements have established long-lasting networks of power, each new protest becoming a building block for street level activism in cities around the globe.

For many artists living in regions where upheaval is chronic and war is the ongoing backdrop to their lives, creating an aesthetic out of a constant state of anxiety is both a necessity and relief. Fighting helplessness in the face of rampant disorder, they take action through artwork that critiques and reimagines the surrounding society, exploring the role of art and their own roles as artists in developing a visual language to articulate moral and political currents. Walid Raad mixes the repressed hysteria of growing up during Lebanon's civil wars (1975–1990) with high art, creating a fabricated but entirely feasible cache of photographs, video, texts, drawings and artwork to represent this combative period. Under the Aegis of The Atlas Group, Raad presented an extensive fictionalized archive of museum and gallery installations. Using wall displays and vitrines, and often including staged performance-lectures within the installations, Raad gives powerpoint presentations or guided tours of the archive material and the ideas that obsess him: art, politics, economics, war, desire, morality and ethics. In *Walkthrough*, 2015, a 55-minute performance as part of an ongoing project *Scratching on Things I Could Disavow*, he expresses mounting levels of frustration at the importation of art fairs and biennials, with their arcane commercial appeal and values, into the Arab art world. For Raad, live performance is the essential connective tissue between the many different kinds of art objects that he makes, allowing him to speak about the significance of each. Indeed, it is an indispensable vehicle for him to voice his complicated worldview.

Artists in Israel, Palestine, Afghanistan, Lebanon, Kazakhstan, Bangladesh and Mexico, including Yael Bartana, Sigalit Landau, Lida Abdul and Teresa Margolles similarly choose to make performances in tandem with work in other media, due to the multitude of complex perspectives that this allows. How to present as artwork a proposal as outlandish as a call for millions of Jewish Polish nationals, displaced during the Holocaust, to return to Poland (Yael Bartana)? Or as improbable as changing the outcome of a sham court case in Iran such that poets, artists and musicians are celebrated for their infinite imagination and not condemned for their liberal beliefs (Shirin Neshat)? Such urgent appeals to upend history, to change situations from negative to positive, can best be articulated in all their complexity through live performance,

DERRICK ADAMS
One Nation Under a Groove of
Instruction, *2012.*
Studio Museum, New York.

in scenes that confront the underlying mercilessness of real
events. For it is the licence to draw on a range of media
without restriction that allows artists to rearrange the facts,
to imagine reconciliation, to create poetic spaces for personal
visions, cultures and rituals.

While many of the artworks discussed in this chapter
come to be known in the international art world through
video installations, the *liveness* at the heart of the original
dramas power through the limitations of any fixed screen.
Performed with non-actors, whether around bombed-out ruins
of buildings in Afghansistan (Lida Abdul) or interventions
on the streets of Kabul (Aman Mojadidi), the actual events of
the piece might take place over many days, even though the
5- or 6-minute film, cut and edited for exhibition, is presented
as 'the work'. Yet, ultimately, the two are inextricable, for the
form and content of the film-to-be is embedded in the premises
of such live performances, with their abstract experimental
approach to narrative, frequent focus on architecture and
bodies, and staging as sculpture or installation. The film
itself becomes a kind of shard – evidence of a step-by-step
process, with each step along the way being aesthetically and
conceptually whole. The final film installation, edited and
sized for projection in a gallery, and not for release in a cinema,
would be entirely different were it the product of even the
most experimental filmmaker.

The transition from performance to film might occur
in reverse, as in the case of Shirin Neshat's *OverRuled*, 2011,
which used an earlier video, *The Last Word,* 2003, as its script
and storyboard. Transposing the set of the original to a stage,
with the same black and white palette and same white-maned
actor, towering in his authority as judge and interrogator,
Neshat expanded on *The Last Word*'s central tenet – the
struggle for freedom of speech in contemporary Iran. Neshat
updates the idea to incorporate the Green Movement with its
hoped-for democratic reforms that in 2009 exploded across
the country and the internet, and were violently suppressed by
the regime in Tehran. For the artist, the collective experience
of the audience 'entering' the space of the video redefined the
ways in which artists might engage and communicate with
audiences. The event constituted its own form of activism
in bringing together politics and art in a staged performance
for the general public.

The shared experience of live performance adds a dimension to contemporary art that has been growing steadily over the past several decades. Audiences now desire close proximity to artists and their working process, and the corollary is that artists get to watch audiences in the act of viewing. As is often said, the viewer completes the work. Direct impact is the hoped-for effect of artists wishing to communicate pressing issues in under-served neighbourhoods – connection to community through aesthetic means. William Pope.L gathers people around him in a host of provocative actions to measure the social and political strains of being black in America. *The Black Factory,* 2005, took place in a large truck decked out as a mobile exhibition and performance space. Moving from Memphis to Missouri, it picked up followers en route who were asked to contribute symbols of blackness to the on-the-go collection. *Pull!,* 2013, a 72-hour collective action comprising teams of fifteen people, who together pulled a truck for 25 miles through the city of Cleveland, was, the artist declared, a ceremony of 'shared labour', considered a catalyst for future action. Transforming an abandoned building, remodelling it brick-by-brick with help from neighbours, and turning it into a generative hub for engagement around a set of activities – an art studio, a library, a vinyl record repository, a kitchen, a screening room – was Theaster Gates' first foray in 2009 into 'social practice'. This gathered steam as he gained sophistication in the machinations of city politics, interfacing with realtors, bankers and collectors to support him in various capacities, rehabilitating several buildings and gradually taking over a street, now known as Dorchester Projects, in the blighted Grand Crossing neighbourhood of South Side Chicago. Sixteen years earlier, in 1993, Rick Lowe, a painter, became an active presence in Houston when he took charge of twenty-two abandoned wooden houses in the Third Ward, creating Project Row Houses, with eight of the shacks designated as exhibition and studio spaces and seven set aside for the Young Mothers Residential programme. The project has since grown to forty-nine buildings spread over ten blocks. In 2015 in Leimert Park, Los Angeles, painter Mark Bradford opened Art + Practice with philanthropist Eileen Norton and neighbourhood activist Allan di Castro, using their combined visionary zeal to shape yet another kind of urban art practice. With 371 square metres (4,000 sq ft) of exhibition space for museum-quality exhibitions, job training facilities, mental health and social services, and a curatorial partnership with the Hammer Museum in Westwood, the fully equipped centre opened in a building close by the hair salon that Bradford's mother owned, and where he had worked as a hairdresser throughout his teens and during studies at CalArts. For Bradford, Art + Practice brought art home to his neighbourhood, a significant cultural experience for Leimert Park residents that did not require a bus trip to a distant part of Los Angeles.

For these artists, success is underscored by a moral imperative that recognizes both the power of art and their power as artists in a thriving international market. While each acknowledges the inspiring activism of Joseph Beuys' propositions for an art of social practice, or 'social sculpture' as Beuys called it in the 1970s, which at that time was more closely aligned with utopian currents in art and society, and which had little to do with an art market that was then at a particularly low ebb, they fully recognize the responsibility attached to their actions and their capacity for exploiting their vaulted positions in the high-finance art world of today. Because of their indisputable aesthetic excellence and critical recognition as leading art world figures, all three have access to a class of patrons and city players, which they use to fuel their activism, and to produce their highly imaginative and game-changing initiatives.

For Beijing-born Ai Weiwei, the correlation between marketplace and activism is far more tenuous, and dangerous.

In opposition to the way that the American artists' privileged positions allow them to act with generosity and to be praised and publicly celebrated, including by local politicians, the Chinese artist receives no such accolades in his native country. While his success in the international art world could be said to provide him with the thinnest protective film, if only because his mistreatment by the authorities is reported worldwide, even so, they act with impunity. He has been under constant watch, physically attacked, his Shanghai studio – built as an education centre – demolished in a day, his mobility taken away from him. In 2011 he was arrested and held in a jail in Beijing for eighty-one days, at which time his passport was withdrawn and only returned four years later. Handcuffed to a chair, interrogated for hours and watched over by two guards day and night, he memorized in excruciating detail the suffering and humiliation that he experienced, reconstructing it for all to see in realistic dioramas at the Venice Biennial two years later. Presented in six large metal containers, visitors could peer through a mailbox-sized opening to see a claustrophobic miniature of his life in prison in six scenes. *S. A. C. R. E. D.* (Supper, Accusers, Cleansing, Ritual, Entropy, Doubt), 2011–13, provided a shocking record of his incarceration, only barely indicating the intense vulnerability of this singular activist in a society where individuality and liberal thinking is vehemently opposed and excised by government forces. To describe the total arc of Ai Weiwei's work and his engagement with assistants, volunteers and the public in responding to and resisting repression is to examine the work of an artist who traverses disciplines, and whose every action, sculpture, photograph or installation, with its profound and pointed content, vastly expands the idea of art activism.

Such ethically driven artwork comes from a sense of urgency to change the minds of people who consider themselves to be far removed from issues of race, class or

REGINA JOSÉ GALINDO
¿Quién Puede Borrar las Huellas?, 2003.
Guatemala City.

ZACKARY DRUCKER, WU
TSANG AND MARIANA
MARROQUIN
P. I. G., 2009.
REDCAT, Los Angeles.

gender, and to give public support to those suffering under the weight of such disregard. Building on identity politics and the culture wars of the 1980s and '90s, a generation of lesbian, gay, bisexual and transgender (LGBT) artists, who have come of age since the mid-aughts, use a multitude of media – performance, photography, film, installation, cabaret – and a range of outlets – museums, biennials and the internet – to develop a burgeoning vocabulary of styles and critical thought. Legal and political shifts have brought this subject matter to the fore in all aspects of social life, as politics and protest have nudged each other forwards into courtrooms and inside the halls of government to bring about change. Same-sex marriage, same-sex parenting, insurer-funded transgender operations, openly gay politicians, CEOs and celebrities in transition are covered by the mainstream media, while Hollywood movies, prime-time television and fashion advertising feature gay and transgender lives in a constantly evolving and highly visible landscape. Many of the visual artists who are mining this material do so using autobiography as a starting point, but some also investigate the subject matter from an historical perspective, revealing material from the past even as they inject it into the present, creating new iconic markers to tell this powerful story.

For Sharon Hayes, speech itself, with a focus on the language of 20th-century protest groups, forms the content of an oeuvre distributed across a range of platforms – room-sized installations that include videos, photographs, posters, album covers and podiums for impromptu speeches; a protest march on the Lower East Side; a monologue on a mid-town street at the entrance to a corporate headquarters where, microphone in hand, she addresses 'a lover' – no one in particular, but someone whom any passer-by might claim to be. She blends historic and current slogans to make critical points about gender, sexuality and race using, for instance, the words of lesbian activist Anna Ruling, 'What Interest Does the Women's Movement Have in the Homosexual Question?', presented at a conference in Berlin in 1904, or the Civil Rights cry 'I Am A Man', from the Memphis Sanitation strike of 1968, to 're-speak' to present day audiences, accounting also for future audiences in that each project is fully documented audio-visually. Bogotá-born and New York-based Carlos Motta, who speaks of growing up amid real violence in a deeply religious and conservative society in 1980s Colombia, also mines political history for language as a starting point for his photographs, documentary-style film installations and community meetings. Presenting these as exhibitions that he describes as 'puncturing the institution', he manipulates the museum and gallery context, as well as his own privilege as an established international artist, to profit from these institutions' high visibility. *Gender Talents*, 2015, an archive of video portraits of trans and intersex activists from four countries, Colombia, Guatemala, India and the United States, was both a screening and a panel discussion – a staged conference of sorts presented at the Spanish Cultural Centre during the 19 Bienal de Arte Paiz in Guatemala. Motta's invitation to more than two hundred trans-women and sex workers gave participants the opportunity to air the needs of a community that had been largely ignored to a broad cross section of invitees, including NGOs, local politicians and the press.

Juliana Huxtable uses language to accelerate her investigation into online libraries, histories and internet aesthetics in ways that few have done so far. She clicks on an extensive menu of references – theory, philosophy, political history – from Kant and Hegel, Judith Butler, Frantz Fanon, Georges Bataille, Frederick Douglass, and Luce Irigaray, to video games and poetry, playing each reference against the other. A talented DJ and member of the House of Ladosha – a black and Latino voguing collective based in Brooklyn but performing in venues globally – she picks up back beats and breaks, matching new meanings to found online images, and juxtaposing historical and contemporary figures from Black and Queer history as well as from her own fictional creations. In *There Are Certain Facts That Cannot Be Disputed*, 2015, her first performance installation staged for a museum, she created a panorama of texts, cut up and pasted on the walls, from her own accumulated library of online research, and texts such as Chancellor Williams' *The Destruction of Black*

Civilization: Great Issues of a Race from 4500 BC to 2000 AD. She invited collaborators and nightlife regulars – Mitch Moore (video), Elysia Crampton (sound), Sadaf H. Nava (violin and vocals), Joe Heffernan (drums and piano), and Michael Potvin (laser projection and lights) – to join her, all members of a deeply committed and connected community. For Huxtable, whose delirious poster-like graphics play on the drama of her own good looks, and that are sometimes paired with her poetry, online is the true underground, today's equivalent of New York's Downtown avant-garde in the 1970s – a dark, anonymous and private place to explore, invent and operate away from the mainstream.

An ever-expanding community of artists who use their LGBT lives and relationships as a baseline upon which to build their artwork has broken through to new levels of public recognition. A powerful new aesthetics of desire scans across a broad spectrum of disciplines, adding to an image bank of irresistible material that can be tracked through a five-decade-long history, from the seminal exhibition, *Transformer: Aspects of Travesty*, 1974, which included Luciano Castelli, Urs Lüthi, Jürgen Klauke, Luigi Ontani and Katharina Sieverding, to the present. Contemporary choreographers, visual artists, photographers, filmmakers, performers and television producers, including Miguel Gutierrez, Trajal Harrall, Cassils, Catherine Opie, Prem Sahib, Zackary Drucker, Zanele Muholi, A. K. Burns, Wu Tsang, Boy Child, My Barbarian, Kalup Linzy, Jacolby Satterwhite, K8 Harding, Nao Bustamante, A. L. Steiner, among many others, are producing material that grows in its boldness and sophistication as it breathes in the air of attention and critique. These artists continue to expand their frames of reference, building bodies of work that are changing minds now and for the future.

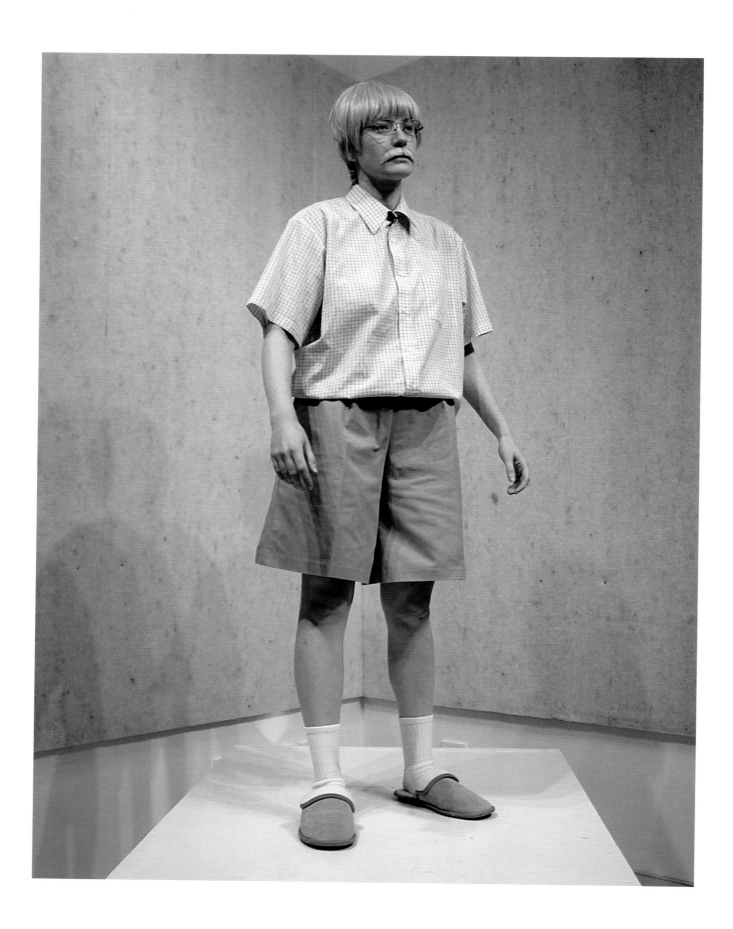

←

TAMY BEN-TOR
Hip Hop Judensau America, *2007.*
Commission for Performa 07, Salon 94, New York.
Photo by Paula Court.

Israeli-artist Tamy Ben-Tor transforms herself into
an array of strange, socially-discomfiting characters in
her performance and video art. In *Judensau*, a series of
cutting, bizarre monologues, she assumes characters
that include a possessed German woman, an ill Swedish
man, and a Jewish dwarf. Donning comically garish
costumes – bowl-cut wigs, decaying yellow teeth,
electric-blue athletic wear – she morphs into each
identity, producing often-spiteful human manifestations
of prejudice and cultural hatred surrounding Judaism.
Drawing its title from a historical form of anti-
Semitic folk art, the series of vignettes is a searing,
reflective critique of nationalism and the stereotypes
of Jewishness that permeate media.

↑

WILLIAM POPE.L
Pull!, *2013.*
Spaces, Cleveland.

Echoing his early *Crawl* works, in which he
crawled the streets of Manhattan to probe the
troubled history of blackness in the United States,
Pope.L's *Pull!* invokes the artist's body as a political
medium but in this case with the aid of the citizens
of Cleveland. The artist invites members of the
public to pull a 10-ton GMC step van for 40 km
(25 miles) over a period of three days from the east
to the west side of Cleveland. This gruelling mobile
performance reflects on the collaborative nature
of labour and the potential of citywide community
performance to instigate new social relations.

WALID RAAD

LEFT ABOVE Scratching on Things I Could Disavow, *2011*.
With actor Carlos Chahine. Museum of Modern Art, New York.

LEFT My Neck is Thinner Than a Hair, *2005.*
The Atlas Group in collaboration with Walid Raad, Bilal Khbeiz and Tony Chakar. Museum of Modern Art, New York.

Lebanese artist Walid Raad's *Scratching on Things I Could Disavow* is a series of 1-hour presentations comprising a powerpoint lecture reporting facts and figures about changing art world economics in the Middle East, and a guided tour through an installation of Raad's artworks. The artist's research-based methodology allows him to outline the impact of art and exhibition practices in the Arab world, questioning the moral and ethical role of a high-stakes art market amid ongoing civil unrest and military campaigns.

ANRI SALA
Dammi i Colori, *2003.*
Film still. Tirana.

In his mesmerizing, rhythmic films Anri Sala investigates
the politics of visual and auditory aesthetics within urban spaces,
often focusing on the legacies of Communism. *Dammi i Colori*
documents the infrastructural evolution and beautification of
Tirana, an Albanian city in post-Communist decay. Proposed
by then-mayor Edi Rama (also an artist), the project coated
the city's blank, decrepit buildings with technicolour paint,
exploring the redemptive, social potential of colour in revitalizing
architecture. Throughout the film Rama meditates on poverty,
community and what it means to project utopia onto crumbling
walls, spoken as shots of the vibrant facades – still luminous at
night – fill the screen.

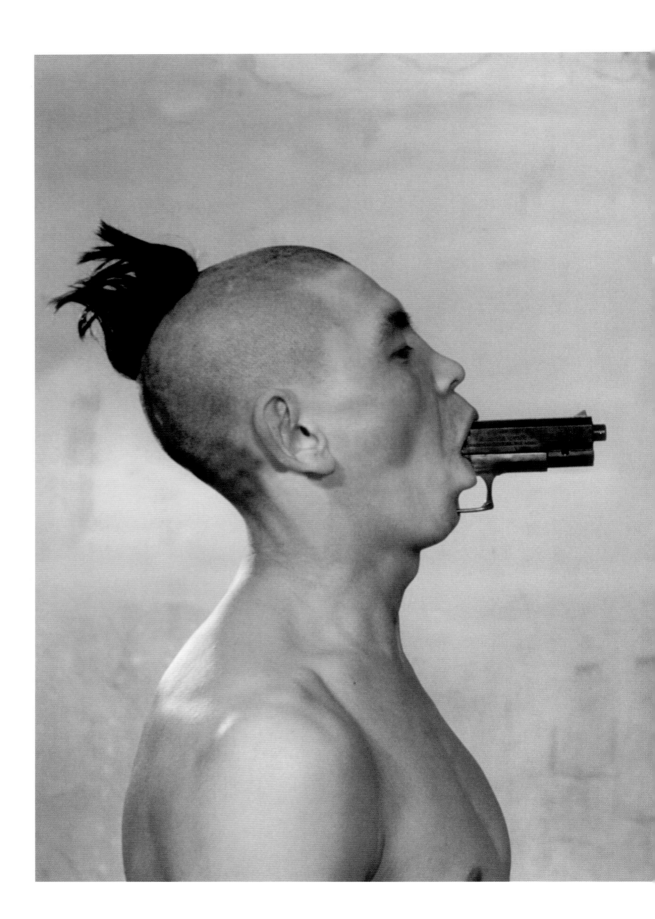

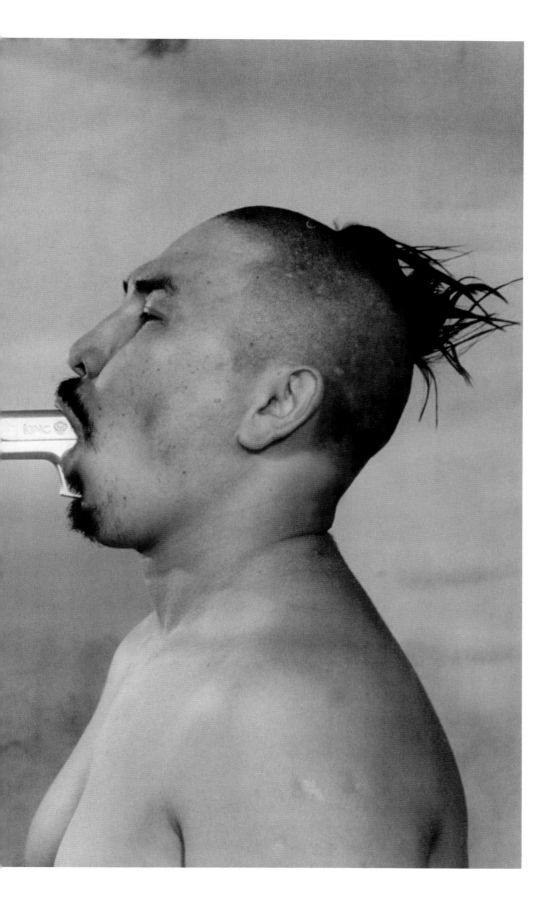

ERBOSSYN MELDIBEKOV
My Brother, My Enemy, *2000.*
*Digital photograph, 100 x 137 cm
(39⅜ x 54 in.). Rossi & Rossi, London.*

Born in Kazakhstan close to the
borders of Kyrgyzstan and Uzbekistan,
and having grown up amid post-Soviet
politics, Erbossyn Meldibekov blends
histories and mythologies that reflect
the multi-ethnic, multi-national
geography of the region. Drawing on
Mongolian-Islamic traditions, rituals
of tribes and clans and anarchic battles
for power, his striking sculptures,
photographs and actions result in
symbolic images that capture the
complex polemics of his world. *My
Brother, My Enemy* conjures the love-
hate relationships between post-Soviet
states under the shadow of Russia's
global dominance.

EMILY ROYSDON
Work, Why Why not, *2008.*
Weld, Stockholm.

Sculptor and activist Emily Roysdon constructs spaces and choreographs people within them to question social structures from a queer and feminist viewpoint. Performers are grouped in a circle, and then as a dancing line or a family portrait – arrangements that audiences can easily identify. Offsetting the silence of the performers, Roysdon engages the audience, asking individuals to respond to key actions. She thus transforms the whole into an activated mechanism that echoes movements and ideas back and forth, subverting the traditionally unilateral relationship between the stage and its viewers.

SIGALIT LANDAU
Barbed Hula, *2000.*
Film still. Tel Aviv.

Israeli artist Sigalit Landau's *Barbed Hula,*
filmed on a beach in Tel Aviv and set to the ambient
sounds of crashing waves, is a powerful metaphor for
the realities of daily life in Israel. A casual, leisurely
activity is also painfully dangerous, in an inseparable
tandem of vulnerability and violence.

SHIRIN NESHAT
OverRuled, *2011.*
Commission for Performa 11 featuring Mohammed Ghaffari, New York.
Photos by Paula Court.

OverRuled, a live performance based on an earlier video by the artist, *The Last Word*, 2003, uses the same set and cast of characters as the former, but expands the theme of censorship and interrogation of a poet to incorporate the political turmoil of the Green Movement, and the trials and imprisonment of artists and intelligentsia that had occurred just two years earlier. Presented as a dramatization of an Islamic court of theocratic law, *OverRuled* draws parallels between justice and religious extremism in medieval and contemporary Iran. The audience, 'the jury', bears witness to an ensemble of thirty-nine actors and five musicians, including renowned singer and composer Mohsen Namjoo.

RABIH MROUÉ
The Pixelated Revolution Performance, *2013.*
Commission for Documenta 13, Staatstheater, Kassel.

Rabih Mroué's staged lecture-performances are an accumulation of information and knowledge that grow increasingly more layered and dense from performance to performance. Presenting each work as a chapter in an ongoing narrative about the history and violence of the Lebanese wars, the Arab Spring, or the unending Syrian Revolution, Mroué manipulates still images, videos, online posts by civilians, newscasters and governments – some fact, some fiction. In *The Pixelated Revolution*, the artist performs as editor, translator, scriptwriter, witness and actor. With a stream of edited material projected on a large screen behind him, he comments on the cinematic limitations of what the audience sees, applying film theories such as Lars von Trier and Thomas Vinterberg's rules of Dogme 95 – no fabricated locations, no added soundtrack, no superficial action – to pictures from the street that make such rules redundant.

EMILY JACIR
Material For a Film (Performance), *2006.*
ABOVE *installation views.*
OPPOSITE *live performance. Commission for Sydney Biennale.*

Meditating on global migration, cultural perception, and Palestine's political turmoil through film, installation and performance, Emily Jacir has been developing an ongoing series, *Material for a Film*, since 2004, as both a eulogy and scrapbook for Wael Zwaiter – a Palestinian translator assassinated in 1972 by Israeli operatives. In this 2006 performance and installation, she enters a shooting range and fires at one thousand white, blank books, later assembling them as a minimalist installation. Using a .22 calibre pistol – the same gun that killed Zwaiter – Jacir memorializes both his unfinished translation of *One Thousand and One Nights* and the violence enacted in his killing.

LIDA ABDUL
LEFT ABOVE What We Saw Upon Awakening, 2006.
Film still. Kabul.
LEFT White House, 2005.
Film still. Kabul.

Having fled Afghanistan as a child to return decades later, Lida Abdul meditates on the traumas of migration, destruction and cultural displacement through video and film. Her 6-minute video *What We Saw Upon Awakening* shows a dreamlike scene of ruin. The bombed, war-torn skeleton of a Kabul home stands, a web of white rope attached to it. Dressed in black, young men pull endlessly at the ropes, their bodies contorting as they struggle with the architecture's weight and the lasting burden of its history. Eventually four men wrap a stone in cloth to bury it, removing it from sight. It's presence, however, still lingers beneath them all. In *White House*, Abdul brushes the wreckage of a bombed presidential complex outside Kabul with white paint – a visual metaphor for the 'white-washing' of the American occupation of Afghanistan.

DERRICK ADAMS
Pablo Fanque's Circus Royal/SIDESHOW, *2015.*
Performa Hub, New York.
Photos by Paula Court.

In vibrant collages, sculpture and live performance, Derrick Adams pays tribute to Britain's first black circus owner Pablo Fanque (1796–1871) in his fantastical, black-and-white portable circus tent. Adams, as ringmaster, directs a 4-hour variety show of musical interludes, magicians, jugglers, readings from writers such as James Baldwin and songs from Erykah Badu. Simultaneously performance and live broadcast radio show, this animated assemblage introduced Fanque's little-known history as equestrian, entrepreneur and source for the line 'for the benefit of Mr. Kite' in John Lennon's *Sgt. Pepper's Lonely Hearts Club Band* in a meditation on black culture, voyeurism and the radical possibilities of carnival-style performance.

TEHCHING HSIEH
One Year Performance (Cage Piece), *1978–79.*
Tribeca, New York.

Tehching Hsieh's *One Year Performance* was a series of five durational performances, each lasting one year, that took place between 1978 and 1984. In these, art and life converge in self-imposed situations where the artist lives and is shaped by the decisions of his art-making. He spent one year locked in a cage, another punching a time clock hourly, the next never going indoors, another tied to someone else without ever touching them, and the last without making art, seeing art, reading or speaking about art or setting foot in a museum or gallery. The works were exercises in extremes of duration and struggle, tedium and discipline, reflexively commenting on performance as itself a boundary between our everyday actions and artificial behaviour. In 2009 the cage was rebuilt and the punch clock and films reinstalled as the series was exhibited at the Museum of Modern Art, reinstating the artist and helping to bolster an interest in the reconstruction of performance as a critical form of historical reference.

←
FRANCIS ALŸS
The Green Line, *2004.*
Film still. Jerusalem.

Trained as an architect and urbanist in his native Belgium, Mexico City-based Alÿs creates performances that frequently involve walks through cities. In *The Leak*, which took place in São Paulo in 1995, he dripped blue paint from a can wherever he walked in the neighbourhood around his gallery. In 2004, he re-enacted this performance in Jerusalem with a leaking can of green paint, following the Green Line that runs through the city, and that was established in 1948 as a temporary armistice agreement between Israel and Jordan. 'Sometimes Doing Something Poetic Can Become Political, and Sometimes Doing Something Political Can Become Poetic' was the title of an exhibition of this work that included a film made of the walk, drawings and maps of the Green Line, and video interviews with people responding to Alÿs' walk as he made his way through a divided Jerusalem. For Alÿs, the question as to whether a poetic act can have political impact or vice versa remains.

AMAN MOJADIDI
Payback, *2009.*
Film stills. Kabul.

Of Afghan descent and born in Florida,
Aman Mojadidi lived and worked in Kabul
for nine years, exploring what he calls the
'geography of self'. Using humour to examine
war-torn life in Afghanistan, he designed
'bling' accessories for jihadi terrorists,
and created events such as *Payback* where,
impersonating a police offer, he set up a fake
roadblock and stopped drivers to give them
each $2, the average cost of a police bribe,
instead of demanding it.

WU TSANG
Damelo Todo, *2011.*
Film still. Los Angeles.

This 20-minute film and accompanying performance,
based on a short story by Raquel Gutiérrez about a fictional
refugee from the Salvadorean Civil War, take place in
Silver Platter, a Latino trans bar in the MacArthur Park
neighbourhood of Los Angeles that has long provided
a haven for local artists, transgender performers and
undocumented immigrants. For several years Wu Tsang
held weekly parties at the bar, including drag shows and
impromptu performances. The film and performance are
interchangeable: film provides an extravagant backdrop to
performance, while performance generates material for film.

PUSSY RIOT
Punk Prayer, *2012*.
Red Square, Moscow.

In 2012, Russian Punk activists Pussy Riot seized the sanctuary of Moscow's Cathedral of Christ the Saviour with a full-blown rendering of their protest song *Punk Prayer – Mother of God, Chase Putin Away!*, calling on the Virgin Mary to join the feminist cause and to oust Vladimir Putin from power. Three members of the group were arrested and convicted of hooliganism and religious hatred. They were imprisoned for two years.

COCO FUSCO

A Room of One's Own: Women and Power in the
New America, 2006–08.
Work in progress first shown at Performa 05, The Kitchen, New York.
Photo by Paula Court.

An artist, writer, educator and performer, Fusco's incisive texts
from the past several decades, focusing on gender, race, colonialism
and power structures, deeply inform the eloquence and poise of her
performances, in person or on video. Intellectually astute but also
accessible, each production introduces the viewer to the extensive
research that inspires her work, while her stylized lecture-performances,
dense with factual information, are also tense with the emotional
impact of raw material. 'To shed light on the art of interrogation' opens
the performance *A Room of One's Own,* examining the special tactics
deployed by female interrogators, and showing how Virginia Woolf's
'room' – as a metaphor for the power and independence of women
to make their own way – can also be used as a space for torture and
aggression when the roles of power and submission are reversed.

OMER FAST
Talk Show, *2009.*
Commission for Performa 09, Abrons Arts Center, New York.
Photo by Paula Court.

In *Talk Show*, Fast translates his complex film installations
– precision-edited to reveal multiple facets of a story, and as
many stories within the story as there are tellers – into his
first live performance. Staged on a mock-up TV talk show
set before an audience, and using the game of 'telephone' as
its underlying structure, the evening begins with a speaker
recounting a personal experience while an actor listens and
passes the story on to two additional actors, twisting the
facts with each telling, before the original speaker returns to
reclaim his story and reveal his identity. On one evening, this
was David Kaczynski, the Unabomber's brother.

Jews!

NATIONALIZM = TERROR

my dead tongue

YAEL BARTANA
And Europe Will be Stunned, *2007–11.*
Film stills.

Bartana's dramatic three-part film installation was the end result of a series of public ceremonies, conferences and communal rites that she staged as part of her investigation into notions of 'homeland', 'return', 'displacement' and 'nationhood'. She addressed these ideas in relation to her native Israel, as well as in a global context. In Part I, '*Mary Koszmary*' (Nightmares), a campaign speech by a young politician for fictional group 'The Jewish Renaissance Movement' is delivered in the style of propaganda films, calling for the return to Poland of millions of Polish Jews displaced during the Holocaust.

**ZACKARY DRUCKER, WU TSANG AND
MARIANA MARROQUIN**
P. I. G., *2009*.
REDCAT, Los Angeles.

A collaboration between LGBT activists and artists
Zackary Drucker, Mariana Marroquin and Wu Tsang,
P. I. G. (an acronym for Politically Involved Girls) is a staging
of film and live performance contemplating contemporary
trans politics, and the civil rights movements that came
before it. Under the guise of a group meeting, the performers
riff on Andy Warhol's satiric film *Women in Revolt*, which stars
three trans actresses who decide to join a women's rights
group. Drucker, Marroquin and Tsang's meeting, featuring
video by Rhys Ernst, is both comedic and intensely personal
– a confrontation of social perception and an expression of
community, gathering and the power of shared experience.

PHIL COLLINS
They Shoot Horses, *2004.*
Film still. Ramallah.

Phil Collins, whose work often focuses on cultural
identities and how they are formed, orchestrated a disco
marathon for youths in Ramallah, where the Israeli-
Palestinian crisis is the constant backdrop to their lives. The
7-hour performance and video (including power outages and
time out for prayer) points to entertainment as a momentary
respite from dire political duress. The title refers to Sydney
Pollack's film *They Shoot Horses, Don't They?* (1969) about
marathons during the Depression.

CARLOS MOTTA
Patriots, Citizens, Lovers..., *2015.*
Installation view. PinchukArtCentre, Kiev.

Responding to political oppression and social marginalization through activism, performance and documentary-based art, Carlos Motta produced *Patriots, Citizens, Lovers...*, an urgent, critical series of interviews on the invisibility, as well as the collective strength, of Ukrainian LGBTI and queer individuals, and the systematic challenges they face. Against vibrant yellow and blue backdrops – the colours of the Ukraine flag – eleven activists vocalize the persistent marginalization, discrimination and danger inherent to their public existence. Some obscure their faces for fear of attack. The videos – life-sized and directly confronting the viewer – reject the misrepresentation of a community, countering a government rhetoric that declares LGBTI and queer individuals to be unpatriotic and unworthy of equality.

ALEJANDRO GONZÁLEZ IÑÁRRITU

Carne y Arena, *2017.*
BELOW *promotional image.*
BOTTOM *installation view. Prada Foundation, Milan.*

Celebrated for his riveting, poetic cinematography and films that examine brutal, survivalist human experience, Academy Award-winning director Alejandro González Iñárritu created *Carne y Arena*, a harrowing, visceral hybrid of installation, virtual reality (VR), and re-enactment centred at the edge of the United States–Mexico border. Upon removing their shoes in a cold, run-down holding cell, viewers are outfitted in VR equipment, digitally emerging somewhere in the Sonoran Desert. They find themselves stranded in the dangerous, barren passageway that many Latin American immigrants do attempt in crossing the border. Over the course of 6½ minutes, viewers experience the frightening chaos of military encroachment: a helicopter flies overhead, vehicles swarm and viewers are held at gunpoint and forced to the ground. Some visitors kneel reflexively, the environment simulating the traumatic, haunting experience immigrants face daily.

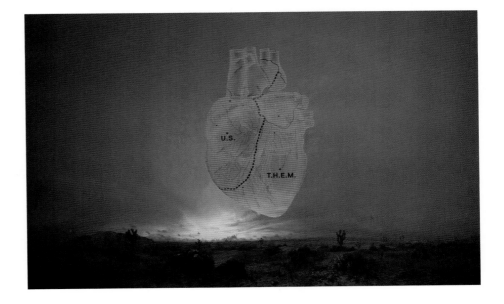

CASSILS
Becoming an Image Performance Still No. 8, *2013*.
Commission for SPILL Festival, National Theatre Studio,
London.

In physically demanding, often laborious performances,
bodybuilder and performer Cassils exerts the body as a medium
and a tool for critiquing gender perception and presentation.
The ongoing series *Becoming An Image* places the artist against
a mass of clay – 1,500 pounds and roughly their height – which
they beat as though in a boxing match. Designed for the camera
and staged in a pitch-black room, the performance was lit only
by the photographer's flash, the artist and audience seeing brief,
fleeting glimpses of the clay's evolution. Exhausting themselves
to form the clay, they shape both the sculpture and themselves
– alluding to the fluidity of bodies and the violence enacted
against transgender individuals.

JULIANA HUXTABLE
There Are Certain Facts That Cannot
Be Disputed, *2015.*
Co-Commission for Performa 15 with the Museum
of Modern Art, New York.
Photo by Paula Court.

With ribbons of anthropological, back-lit text
draped from the walls, musicians in period costume and
video playing behind her, DJ, nightlife icon and writer
Juliana Huxtable staged her first live performance in a
museum context. This three-act performance interrogates
the individual's relation to marginalized histories and the
subversive power of the digital. The gripping, poetic epic
voiced the potential of the virtual as a radically inclusive
archive while confronting its ephemerality. Dressed in 18th-
century undergarments, the artist speaks of whitewashed
antiquity and the flawed, yet vital, hope that an electronic
utopia holds to correct and alter accepted histories.

MARTIN CREED
Work No. 1020, 2009.
Commission for Frieze Art Fair, Sadler's Wells, London.

During this 70-minute performance, five basic ballet
positions are performed in meticulous repetition by five
trained dancers, to live music played by Martin Creed and a
small band. As a visual artist making a dance, Creed is able to
create both an acutely focused and unabashedly open process
for the audience to witness, at times stopping everything
to introduce the dancers and talk about the meaning of the
work. For him, this was about revealing the limitations of
movement and its dependence on music.

RASHAAD NEWSOME
Shade Compositions, *2009.*
The Kitchen, New York.
Photos by Paula Court.

Rashaad Newsome investigates the body and its
relation to media perception, social respect and
political consumerism in his visually decadent collages,
live performance and video. In *Shade Compositions*, he
recycles socially demeaning stereotypes of black women's
vocalizations, interjections and gestures – tongue clicking,
hands on hips, 'Excuse!'. Using a video-game controller as a
baton, Newsome leads more than twenty-five women in the
makeshift orchestra, recording and remixing their sounds
and motions live. The synchronized, near-mechanical actions
produce a visually and sonically fascinating symphony that
interrogates the choreographies of racial prejudice.

AI WEIWEI

S. A. C. R. E. D., *2011–13.*

Installation view. Collateral event at Venice Biennale.

Celebrated for his political engagement, activism and disruptive conceptual art, the iconic Chinese artist Ai Weiwei built *S. A. C. R. E. D.* – a harrowing, visceral installation depicting his eighty-one-day incarceration in solitary confinement. Six enormous, foreboding iron boxes were placed in a Venetian church, each containing a gruelling scene from his daily life in jail – Supper, Accusers, Cleansing, Ritual, Entropy, Doubt. During his incarceration Weiwei was monitored constantly by two guards, and each scene shows him stripped of privacy as he ate, slept and defecated. Peering into each scene through small holes in metal boxes, the audience become as voyeuristic as the guards, watching and making a spectacle of his deeply exposed but confined life.

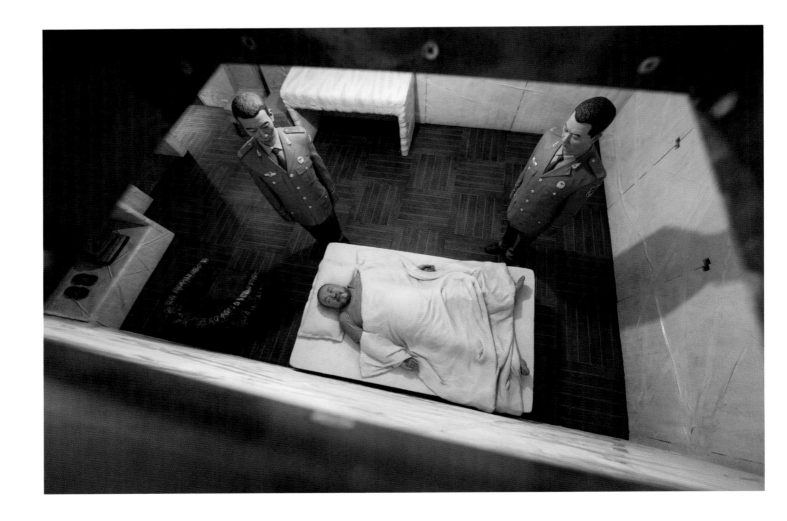

REGINA JOSÉ GALINDO
¿Quién Puede Borrar Las Huellas?, 2003.
Guatemala City.

Acknowledging the victims of the Guatemalan civil war that
lasted from 1960 to 1996 with her confrontational, vulnerable
performance and body art, Regina José Galindo memorializes the
estimated twenty thousand civilians killed with her performance
¿Quién Puede Borrar Las Huellas? Barefoot, Galindo walks from the
Court of Constitutionality to the National Palace in Guatemala City,
soaking her feet in a basin of animal blood that she carries with her.
Walking past fruit vendors, crowds and her unknowing audience, she
stains the sidewalk with each step – footprints that would be both
seen and ignored. Upon reaching the palace she leaves her final prints
at the door, abandoning the basin on the ground and walking away.

←

TERESA MARGOLLES
What Else Could We Talk About?, *2009.*
Commission for the Venice Biennale. Palazzo Rota-Ivancich.
Photo by the artist.

In the Rota-Ivancich Palace in Venice, Teresa Margolles installs a grisly scene of violence, death and loss. Large banners made of cloth used to mop up the remains at sites of gunfights and murder in Culiacán, Mexico – a city rife with drug trafficking – cover the elegant walls of the palace and hang from flag poles. Against this backdrop, the floors are intermittently mopped by relatives of the dead, using water containing traces from the crime scenes, including the blood of victims. Margolles' powerful public rage against torture and death stands in stark contrast to Mexico's feeble attempts at law enforcement to contain the horrors.

↑

CLIFFORD OWENS
Nsenga Knight, *2011.*
Photograph as part of 'Anthology' exhibition of
performance. Museum of Modern Art, New York.

Clifford Owens' 'Anthology' is a series that strives to grant greater visibility to African-American performance and its history, nodding to its neglect in institutional settings and scholarly discourse. Soliciting a series of performance scores – instructions for performative actions – from a group of twenty-six celebrated African-American artists, the project serves as both an exercise and compendium of under-represented performance practice; a personal and physical anthology acted out by Owens, presented live and documented in exhibition form. Nsenga Knight, an interdisciplinary conceptual artist and filmmaker, provided the score for Owens' performance.

ANDREA GEYER, SHARON HAYES, ASHLEY HUNT, KATYA SANDER AND DAVID THORNE
Combatant Status Review Tribunals pp. 002954–003064: A Public Reading, *2012.*
Museum of Modern Art, New York.

Sitting at four tables arranged in a makeshift square, surrounded by an audience of museum-goers, nine performers present a 4-hour public reading of unedited transcripts from tribunals held at the Guantanamo Bay detention centre between July 2004 and March 2005. The tribunals, which determined whether detainees met criteria that deemed them 'enemy combatants', are recited by the readers, who cycle through each judicial position as the reading progresses. Jointly organized by several artists, the performance illuminated often-obscured, privatized governmental proceedings in an effort to make public knowledge otherwise denied to citizens.

OTOBONG NKANGA
DIAOPTASIA, *2015.*
Tate Modern, London.

Through sculpture, drawing and performance, Otobong Nkanga interrogates the human relation to landscape and displacement. *DIAOPTASIA* – broadcast live via Tate Modern's performance room – is a meditation on the fracture and manipulation of physical and linguistic material. Nkanga wears a braided copper sculpture in her hair, filled with jagged blue rocks, reminiscent of 1960s Nigerian hairstyles. Bringing photography of a Namibian mine together with written and sung text and the physical puncturing of geometric sculptures, she speaks in both English and Nigerian Pidgin – a culturally-specific manipulation of English. The language is a sliced, hacked dialect, formed by a process reminiscent of stone-mining.

TERRY ADKINS
Sacred Order of the Twilight
Brothers, *2013*.
Performa Hub, New York.
Photos by Paula Court.

Visual artist, writer and musician, Terry
Adkins approaches musical instruments as
sculptures, and sculptures as opportunities
to invent new musical instruments. Arranged
in elegantly shaped installations conceived as
scores, which he calls 'recitals', Adkins' work
is an ongoing interplay between the sonic and
the visual, mixed with a powerful physicality
that radiates from each bold construction. His
custom-built 5.5-metre-tall (18 ft) horns called
Akrhaphones – performed by the multimedia
collaborative Lone Wolf Recital Corps, which
he founded in 1986 with Blanche Bruce – are
part of an arsenal of instruments, including
woodwinds, contrabass, pocket trumpet and
electronics as well as video and spoken word.
The artist uses these to stage emblematic
concerts that are also rich with allusions to
people and places from African-American
history. This performance was the artist's last
before his untimely death three months later.

SANTIAGO SIERRA
Submission, *2009*.
Anapra.

Paying a man to live behind a gallery wall for fifteen days, trading drug-addicted prostitutes the cost of heroin to tattoo lines on their back and casting human excrement are a few examples of controversial, disturbing performances by Santiago Sierra, the artist exposing the exploitation of individuals by exploiting them for his own work. For *Submission* (formerly *World of Fire*, 2006–07), Sierra hired local, unemployed labourers in Anapra, Mexico – an impoverished community on the border with the United States – to dig the word 'SUMISION' into the ground. Originally meant to be set on fire, the word was left as an accusation towards the United States, Mexico and local individuals at all levels of society, raising the essential questions of who submits to whom, and what is being demanded.

CHAPTER 4

Dance After Choreography

In the late 1990s, much of the new choreography to be seen in New York, Paris, Brussels and Berlin could be called 'conceptual dance', both for its rigorous intellectual underpinnings and for the ways in which talking about dance while dancing created a form of lecture in performance as well as deconstructing dance itself. The body was 'material'; the venue, whether black box or proscenium, was 'space'. Watching dance was as much a thought-process as it was a visual or visceral pleasure. It was also just as frequently a history lesson of sorts, for the references to avant-garde dance were many – in particular to the 1960s and '70s Judson Dance Theater and Grand Union in downtown New York. These groups, with their insistence on eliminating all remnants of spectacle, seduction or virtuosity, had so completely separated the making of dance from earlier modern choreographic methods. Working instead with the 'democratic body' as a plain-spoken instrument for questioning the nature of dance and its place in the politicized society of the times, these choreographers collaborated closely with friends and colleagues across disciplines, including sculpture, film, poetry and music. An integrated community of visual artists, filmmakers, writers, composers and choreographers shared their sensibilities (and often living and work spaces) and a conceptual approach to their medium. Each saw their task as creating personalized work that distilled the material of their chosen art form into its essential elements.

ANNE TERESA DE KEERSMAEKER
Work/Travail/Arbeid, *2015.*
Centre Pompidou, Paris.
Photo by Anne Van Aerschot.

WILLIAM FORSYTHE
I Don't Believe in Outer Space, *2011.*
Festspielhaus Hellerau, Dresden.
Photo by Dominik Mentzos.

The dance revolution in 1960s and '70s New York was studied, reimagined and reconstructed some three decades later by a group of young French choreographers, including Christoph Wavelet, Anne Colod, Simon Hecquet and Dominique Brun, who called themselves Quatuor Albrecht Knust (formed in 1993 and named for the 19th-century German choreographer and pedagogue). Their mission was to research and reenact key choreographic works from dance history, including Yvonne Rainer's famous *Trio A* from 1965. These choreographers had grown up during the heyday of French dance theatre in the 1980s, when ambitious works were produced by choreographers such as Maguy Marin, Dominique Baguet, Philippe Decouflé and many more. Visually dazzling and technically of the highest order, each of their large-scale modern ballets were aided by the seemingly unlimited resources provided by the French Ministry of Culture, which throughout the decade would establish National Choreographic Centres in nineteen of the country's twenty-two regions. The intention was to generate an understanding of choreography and dance in cities across France, but also to decentralize the existing focus on the French capital. The

choreographers who were appointed to lead the centres, along with teams of composers, musicians, artists, costume and lighting designers and stage technicians, built a brave new world of dance, developed at the level of national cultural policy. In Germany Pina Bausch's Tanztheater Wuppertal was producing vivid dance theatre at an extraordinary pace, creating material that expanded and deepened Bausch's view of dance as an agglomeration of political geographies and literary and musical references. Anne Teresa De Keersmaeker in Belgium impeccably combined highly conceptual and physical worlds, bringing text, film footage, music and architecture into her rigorous, methodical and emotional investigations of the rhythms and rituals of dance. Each movement or pose – pulsing, turning, jumping, sitting – is measured according to the dimensions of the stage, bodies and chairs. De Keersmaeker built new dance vocabularies with each production, accumulating a body of work rich enough to launch a school for choreographers and dancers in Brussels, P. A. R. T. S – Performing Arts Research and Training Studio – founded in 1995 with La Monnaie Theatre. Graduates of De Keersmaeker's inventive course, having benefited from the incisive research into avant-garde dance that she instigated with an international core of distinguished instructors, have proven some of the most interesting choreographers in Europe this century. These include Meg Stuart, Noé Soulier, Mette Ingvartsen, Eleanor Bauer, David Wampach and many others.

The rich, pan-European dance culture of the late 20th century was nourished by dance festivals in cities across Europe, from Brussels and Rotterdam to Avignon, Frankfurt, Montpelier, Paris and Vienna. These provided not only regular platforms for exposure and criticism, but also places for rehearsals and repeat performances, as well as opportunity for conversations and feedback. Audiences became habituated to incorporating one or more dance festivals into their summer calendars. Such festivals delivered a highly articulate and imaginatively schooled generation of dancers and a public who over many years had accumulated an understanding of the avant-garde strategies and trans-disciplinary references that the choreographers were routinely employing in their productions.

An inventive new generation of French choreographers, trained in classical and contemporary dance but also, surprisingly, in biology, philosophy and literature, emerged in the late 1990s and early 2000s. Emboldened by the creative engines of the many dance centres to examine ever more incisively the meaning of dance and its relationship to audience, in many ways these choreographers set out to question the grand projects of the 1980s. Using intellectual probes forged by such French philosophers of the 1980s as Jacques Derrida, Gilles Deleuze and Jacques Rancière, they shaped a philosophical and poetic sounding board for dance concepts that reflected the physical and mental acuity essential to their medium. By 2005 Jérôme Bel, Xavier Le Roy and Boris Charmatz had emerged as a triumvirate of exceptional thinkers about dance, its history and its execution. Each had an entirely different aesthetic, movement vocabulary and story to tell, though they all shared a commitment to speaking directly to audiences, and having them empathize with both the thinking and doing of the performers in their midst.

For Bel, conceptual art was a resource in the search for new dance frontiers, with its quest – paradoxical in a material world – to give equal value to thinking and doing. He would appropriate the instructions, questions and definitions of the conceptualists into his own literal conversation about dance, so that the verbal exchange of ideas became part of the dance itself. *Pichet Klunchun & Myself,* 2005, was one such demonstration – a casual interview-as-performance of Pichet, a classically trained dancer in Thai tradition, dressed in a black unitard. Bel, himself trained in contemporary dance, conducted the interview casually dressed in a plaid shirt and loose-fitting pants. The pair discussed their personal backgrounds and training as dancers, highlighting the perfection of one and the intentional low-key posture of the other, as well as their very different cultural heritages. Xavier Le Roy, a qualified molecular biologist, who started taking dance classes while

completing a PhD, took to making dance works with a mindset adapted from his training as a research scientist. Blending scientific methods with those of choreography, he explored the effects of each on perception in the viewer. *Self Unfinished,* 1998, his debut on the international dance circuit, involved Le Roy stepping onto a brightly lit stage (bare save for a chair and a table), slowly transforming his body into several forms of 'something else' – a ball, an upright insect with two sets of feet, a chicken without a head. The metamorphoses took almost an hour, focusing viewer attention on the tiniest shifts in Le Roy's thinking process, and providing a foundation for his research into methods in choreography that he would develop over the following years. Starting out in the 1990s, Boris Charmatz created dances in collaboration with fellow choreographer Dimitri Chamblas, and began several other collaborative projects, such as the 'association edna' in 1992, which produced films, plays and performances, and Bocal in 2002 – a nomadic and ephemeral dance school. He worked with writers, artists and musicians, including Julie Chima, Raimund Hoghe, Saul Williams and Archie Shepp. He would also perform with fellow choreographers Bel, De Keersmaeker and Tino Sehgal. By 2009, when he was appointed director of the Centre for Choreography in Rennes, his pedagogical impulses gelled into a bold manifesto, *Musée de la danse,* which would represent the collaborative, think-tank nature of his preferred way of working. Over several years this evolved into a programme that, with its evocative title, would create a ripple effect across disciplines, influencing museum conversations about how to reintroduce dance, with its focus on the body-in-situ, into the trajectory of contemporary art history; in the 1970s, art venues had provided an important viewing space for many in avant-garde dance circles. *Musée de la danse* proposes that the body is a container of dance history, its own portable museum of muscle memory deposited over centuries; it provides an open-ended conversation for the ways in which dance may be framed and perceived, but also a limitless repertoire of references from hundreds of years of dance from the past.

In the United States, the turn of the century brought a new wave of dance in the form of polemical choreographic visions that were the work of strong individuals, some quite maverick in their approach to constructing dance in vanguard downtown venues of New York. Sarah Michelson, Maria Hassabi, Trajal Harrell, Miguel Gutierrez, Ralph Lemon, Tere O'Connor and Faye Driscoll, among many others, made performances that were distinguished by idiosyncratic personal styles and vocabularies of movement, frequently containing traces of 'contact improv' (a trademark of American dance initiated by Steve Paxton in the 1970s) and each with their own strongly articulated subject matter. Intimate in scale and so particular as to be limited to a small community of dancers, known to each other and having worked together over many years, their material seemed almost untranslatable to larger groups of dancers, in contrast to the schools or centres for choreography that helped sustain their European counterparts.

Sarah Michelson's choreography for a close-knit group of dancers, each with strong personalities of their own, focused on a narrow range of repetitive movements and surprisingly emotional content. Complex layers of lighting, costume, sculpture, painting and hard-driving sound were all conceived and directed by the choreographer herself. Dancers followed exacting instructions down to the level of eye movement, and exhausting, drawn-out sequences characterized performances that each took place within a framework as particular and precise as any architectural blueprint. The venue provides a starting point for all of Michelson's work: how the space might be entirely reconsidered and turned around in performance; how sightlines can be broken, altered and re-directed, making spectatorship of a work feel as intense as its execution. In *Shadowman*, 2003, at The Kitchen, the back of the large 'box' of a theatre became the front and visa versa. The seating area faced the wide garage-style entrance doors, which opened to the sidewalk, with dancers arrayed on the steps of a house across the street. Viewers were given a long view that included the building, casual passers-by and evening traffic coming and going in the middle distance. Almost a decade later, and with a repertoire of breathtaking productions behind her (such as *Dover Beach*, 2009, with its bold architectural divides, sculptural lighting structures, live piano accompaniment and several exquisitely poised pre-teen dancers and *Devotion*, 2001, with its large full-length portrait

painting of the choreographer hanging high above her hard-working dancers, who might be continuously jumping or balancing on one foot for many gruelling minutes), Michelson created *Devotion Study #1 – The American Dancer* in 2012 for the entire fourth floor of the Whitney Museum of American Art in a work commissioned for the Whitney Biennial. Drawing on an arsenal of tried and true elements developed over time, spanning lighting, music, spoken text, visual components (including a large neon portrait of the artist), geometrically cut costumes and a loyal troupe of fiercely energetic dancers, this 90-minute tour de force was a pure expression of Michelson's demanding vision. It also reflected the dancers' devotion to their practice, their bodies honed to produce the choreographer's non-stop stepping movements – in this instance mostly backward and in dizzying circles.

The American dancer celebrated in Michelson's opus conjures a legacy of Judson, but also of Martha Graham, Merce Cunningham, Trisha Brown, Lucinda Childs, Yvonne Rainer and Steve Paxton – the ABC of every young choreographer's career, and essential frame of reference for modern dancers in the United States. Trajal Harrell confronts this history, reconfiguring it to include dance hall and club dancing, in particular the riveting and theatrically brash material of the underground transgender and drag queen 'voguing balls' that took place in Harlem, New York, from the early 1960s, and were made known to a public outside of the immediate neighbourhood through the 1990 documentary *Paris is Burning*. Focusing on competitions between 'houses' of elaborately costumed runway dancers, many of Black and Latino descent, Harrell approached these histories by asking: 'What would have happened in 1963 if someone from the voguing dance tradition in Harlem had come downtown to Judson Church in Greenwich Village to perform alongside the early postmoderns?'. His rhetorical question says as much about the storytelling dimension of history as about the need for a revisionist rewriting of that history in New York if the inventiveness of undermined populations is to be included. Instead of a literal rewrite, however, Harrell creates new dances in a contemporary context, laying down a vocabulary of gloriously mixed sensibilities, from postmodern to ballet to dancehall, runway strutting, cabaret, jazz, funk, rhythm and blues and Butoh, all of which have shaped New York avant-garde dance across all its boroughs and over many decades. *Twenty Looks or Paris is Burning at the Judson Church* proposed

JÉRÔME BEL
Véronique Doisneau, 2004.
Commission by the Paris National Opera.

this radical disruption to the trajectory of time, a project to which Harrell has systematically added, as though to a serial novel, new titles including *Twenty Looks* in five sizes, from extra small (XS) to extra large (XL); *(M)imosa*, 2011; *Antigone Sr.*, 2012; *Judson Church is Ringing in Harlem*, 2013; and *Return of La Argentina*, 2015. He has built, with his cast of elegant dancers, an encyclopedia of movement in the most rigorous, sensual and deeply inventive way.

Tightly packed downtown dance spaces continue to invigorate the New York dance scene, despite real-estate ventures closing in on all sides and the near non-existence of public money for support. These non-profit venues, and the dedicated people who run and constantly fundraise for them, make it possible for new and innovative work to continue to be seen. Since 2010, several of these spaces have begun to produce analytically probing and context-setting programmes. Danspace St Mark's, for example, instigated a series called 'Platform', described as an 'exhibition unfolding over time', by adopting curatorial methods from the art world. Presenting material in such a way as to offer historical overview as well as showing thematic or stylistic connections through a prism of critical analysis and interpretation, such programming functions as a strong educational tool as well as a marketing one, allowing for greater audience accessibility and reach. Curators, often seasoned choreographers themselves, such as seminal figures Ishmael Houston Jones or Ralph Lemon (responsible also for curating a three-week season at the Museum of Modern Art, *Some sweet day*, 2012, that would launch a permanent dance programme at the museum), use these spaces to articulate the complex history of postmodern dance in the last five decades, and the shifting sands of cultural and political history that have shaped it. Publications, seminars, lectures and workshops, regularly featured alongside thematic clusters of performances, are changing the emphasis of such organizations from sites of presentation to curatorial centres of research and debate. Mini festivals such as American Realness, running for a week or ten days at a time, also succeed in maintaining a community of inventive practitioners, in conversation both with each other and with a loyal downtown following, always in search of new meanings for dance in our times.

New performance art programmes in museums around the globe, several of which (including the Museum of Modern Art, the Whitney Museum of American Art and Tate Modern) are taking the lead with substantial dance commissions and 'extended performance exhibitions', will no doubt comment on our times in exciting new ways. They will also support the perennially under-served dance community. Avant-garde dance has never seen such careful archiving before, nor such institutional regard in the form of special acquisition councils or performance committees dedicated to acquiring dance and featuring year-round programming. In addition, the 'frame' of the museum, with its pristine halls and staircases, and audience expectations of production values consistent within the sparkling new architecture of recently built spaces, will provide additional staging possibilities even as, by contrast, they allow dancers to define ever more clearly their relationship to the machinery of theatre – the thrill of backstage, sprung floors and rows of expectant faces looking up at them from seats below.

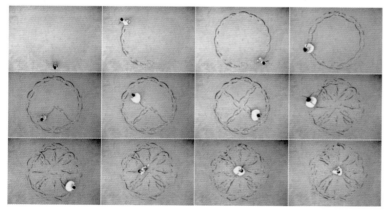

ANNE TERESA DE KEERSMAEKER
Fase, Four Movements to the Music of
Steve Reich, *1982/2011*.
ABOVE *The Tanks, Tate Modern, London.*
LEFT *Museum of Modern Art, New York.*

Choreographed and performed in New York in 1982,
Fase marked De Keersmaeker's remarkable debut in the
New York dance world, also establishing her relationship
to minimalist music and the structure and pulse that
still drive her movements. Almost thirty years later, her
ingenious play of subtly changing forms continues to
provide a mesmerizing visual and conceptual puzzle for
audiences in the intimate space of the museum. *Violin
Phase*, De Keersmaeker's solo from *Fase* performed decades
later, takes on new proportions in MoMA's Marron
Atrium. The bird's-eye view gives a new dimension to this
dazzling and enduring work, while the lines in the sand
show her footwork to be as eloquent and breathtaking as
any hand-drawn design.

TRAJAL HARRELL
Antigone Sr./Twenty Looks or Paris is Burning at
the Judson Church (L), *2012.*
New York Live Arts.
Photo by Miana Jun.

Starting in 2009, Harrell has created a series of
performances of varying lengths that reimagine the history
of dance in the 1960s as a meeting of Harlem's voguing
ballroom scene with the Judson Dance Theater in downtown
New York. Combining dance and street styles, runway
walking, spoken word and song, Harrell's opus of seven
separate productions questions the standard vocabularies of
American contemporary dance, placing issues of race, gender
and identity centre stage.

MICHAEL CLARK
th, *2011*.
Turbine Hall, Tate Modern, London.
Photo by Hugo Glendinning.

Celebrated since the 1980s for his high-energy performances marrying classical dance with punk and other contemporary sensibilities, Clark created this work for the monumental space of Tate Modern's Turbine Hall. *th* mixes eight professional dancers from the choreographer's own company with seventy-eight members of the public, who workshop for several weeks before performing the finished work in full public view during museum hours. The choreographic method involved calibrating mechanical movements for the crowd, and ramping up the scale of the work to match its bold architectural container.

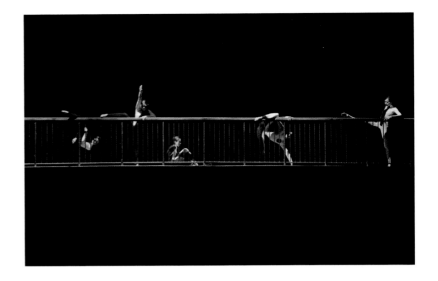

FAYE DRISCOLL
There is so much mad in me, *2010.*
Dance Theater Workshop, New York.

This performance plays with the exasperating
expressiveness of television talk shows as well as the
all-consuming effects of media on daily lives and social
behaviour. Fixated on the 'feedback loop' between performers
and audience, Driscoll makes work that highlights those
relationships, conjuring psychic states through movement,
text, song, props and costumes. Six dancers seated in a row,
as on a television set, each call attention to themselves and
soon peel off into a danced battle of egos with fast and fluid
movements, some quoting downtown dance vocabulary,
others more pop combinations.

MARIA HASSABI
PREMIERE, *2013*.
Commission for Performa 13 with The Kitchen, New York.
Photo by Paula Court.

Maria Hassabi's choreographic work is an obsessive
exploration of minimal movement. The five dancers in
PREMIERE took an entire hour to rotate their positions
almost imperceptibly, ending in the same place as where they
began. Hassabi draws on sculptural references to expand
her own choreographic vocabulary, while at the same time
exposing the fragility of performing bodies. The slowness
of the dancers' movements, including quivering eyelids and
twitching muscles, and the glaring wall of theatre spotlights,
which sharply light the tableau from one side (and heat up
the room), increase the sense of physical endurance for both
performers and audience.

MÅRTEN SPÅNGBERG
La Substance, but in English, *2014*.
Commission for MoMA PS1, Queens, New York.

Staging colourful and intentionally chaotic performances that grapple with commodity overload, media interference and audience indifference, Mårten Spångberg sets up a technicolour dreamscape for close viewing of his accomplished dancers. While sometimes they dance, they just as often sit still, change clothes or meander among scattered everyday objects, plastic marijuana leaves, empty pizza boxes and record players, against a backdrop of fashion logos. Audiences come and go, free to sit on the floor, paint on a large wall behind the dancers, or move to the insistent soundscape of new music and contemporary pop.

RALPH LEMON
Untitled, *2010.*
Archival pigment print from original film.
Little Yazoo, Mississippi.

The work of Ralph Lemon – equal parts dancer, choreographer, writer and visual artist – uses both personal memoir and collective history to construct an anthropology of racism in the United States. Whether performing 'counter-memorials' at lynching sites or dancing with relatives of early blues musicians, Lemon creates work that articulates the high stakes of embodied political relations. These prints from an ongoing project were first included in an exhibition that explored a close friendship and collaboration between the artist and Little Yazoo resident Walter Carter. The images are a seamless component of Lemon's choreographic imagination.

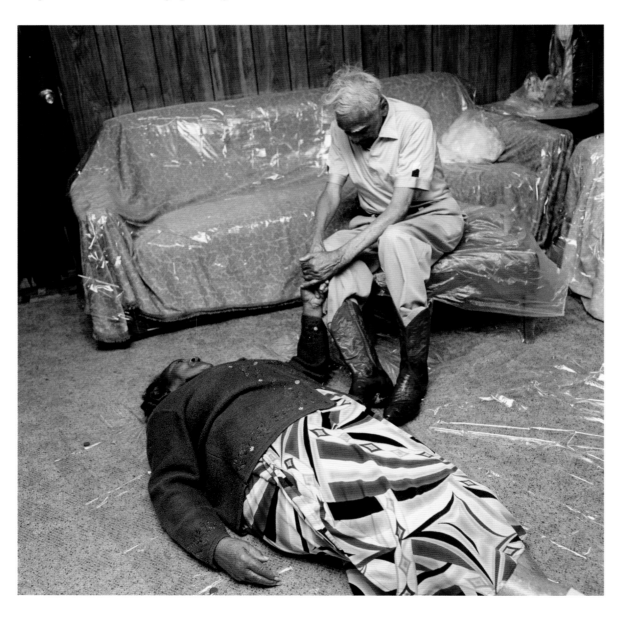

MARIE COOL
FABIO BALDUCCI

Untitled (Prayers), *1999–2007.*
Clocktower Gallery as part of Performa 07,
New York.
Photo by Paula Court.

French choreographer Marie Cool and
Italian visual artist Fabio Balducci have been
combining their respective disciplines since
1995 to create slow and sometimes repetitive
actions with industry-standard objects from
everyday working life. A4 sheets of paper,
scotch tape, cotton thread and other standard
office equipment evoke both administrative
operations and economic structures, while
slow-motion gestures imply a desire to optimize
work processes. Cool, the sole performer of the
duo, presents these highly conceptual actions
either alone or in groups of a dozen or so,
creating quiet 'dramas with a figure' that focus
the viewer's eye on the smallest gestural details,
building an unusual visual memory bank of
imagery over time.

JÉRÔME BEL

ABOVE Disabled Theater, *2013.*
Commission for Documenta 13.
Photo by Paula Court.
LEFT Ballet, *2015. Commission for Performa 15, Marian Goodman Gallery, New York.*
Photo by Paula Court.

Bel's capacity for combining empathy and analysis led the way in a collaboration with Theater Hora, a Zurich-based theatre company of professional actors with learning disabilities. Known for his sensitive portraits exploring the intertwinement of personal and professional lives, Bel's work tackles this subject in terms of the drive to perform. Actors between the ages of eighteen and fifty-one react freely to a series of tasks proposed by the artist, creating a piece, *Disabled Theater*, that is both brutally honest and highly political. Specially devised for the city of New York, *Ballet* unfolded over the course of three weeks, and was presented in three separate venues, offering a different reading for dance in each.

TERE O'CONNOR
BLEED, *2013.*
Danspace Project, New York.
Photos by Paula Court.

O'Connor's approach to dance as a metaphorical language for reflecting on the world in which we live, its terrors and pleasures, has been built over more than three decades. For him, the close-knit family of dancers with whom he collaborates and his own reflection on the nature of consciousness have combined to forge an idiom that recurs from one powerful work to the next. *BLEED*, the culmination of a two-year project involving three earlier works, *Secret Mary, poem* and *Sister* (all with different casts) appears as both a continuation of these and an entirely new hybrid. With a cast of eleven dancers and 'ghosts' of the earlier movement phrases, this finale is in some ways another beginning: the dancers, many of whom are choreographers themselves, keep moving in the mind's eye, waiting for the next production to materialize.

ELAD LASSRY
Untitled (Presence), *2012.*
The Kitchen, New York.
Photo by Paula Court.

For his first live work, *Untitled (Presence)*, Elad Lassry treats performance as mediated experience, presenting ten dancers from the American Ballet Theatre and New York City Ballet as if witnessed through a screen. Using framing devices that recall a lens' aperture and treating reality as pictorial space, the performers are shown cut off and composed, in detail and in full. Questioning the moment where a photographic image becomes artistic expression, Lassry directs the viewer's eye to fix on a particular moment, object or motion, transforming these into iconic symbols elevated beyond mere image. Set against saturated colour and bright light, the dancers are visually flattened in the audience's perceptual field, bringing attention to the rampant mediation of our experiences, and the illusions of stage and image.

PABLO BRONSTEIN
Plaza Minuet, *2007.*
Performa 07, World Financial Center, New York.
Photos by Elizabeth Proitsis.

Bronstein's choreography shapes a temporary architecture out of the dancers' bodies, combining his fascination for 16th-century Baroque dance and architecture, perspective, formal grids and the visual patterns of classic plazas with a contemporary minimalist sensibility. Seventeen ballet dancers perform a 15-minute sequence in four different public plazas around Lower Manhattan, making visceral to passers-by the spatial design of each architectural setting.

ANNE IMHOF
Faust, *2017*.
Commission for the Venice Biennale, German Pavilion.

Fiercely physical, with chiselled arms and ripped muscles, and intensely present, face to face with audience members in an open-ended series of connected galleries, fourteen performers fall, lie, bunch up in a heap or hoist themselves onto pedestals set in the walls of the dramatically scaled building of Venice's German Pavilion. Some are trained dancers, others artists, singers or actors, wearing informal athletic gear, t-shirts and sneakers. Imhof's expressive add-ons to the pavilion's structure – a glass floor with a half-a-metre (2 ft) crawl space below, a tall metal fence enclosing a dog run around the front perimeter of the building for two elegant Doberman Pinschers, glass dividers between rooms, pulleys to reach a high parapet and imposing speakers that blast loud bursts of music – transform the given architecture into an operatic set for the arresting themes of millennial aesthetics and obsession.

**JONATHAN BURROWS &
MATTEO FARGION**

Cheap Lecture, *2009.*
Maasmechelen Cultural Center.
Photo by Herman Sorgeloos.

Cheap Lecture is one of a series of duets – including *Both Sitting Duet, Quiet Duet* and *Speaking Duet* – in which Burrows, a British former soloist with the Royal Ballet, and Fargion, an Italian classical guitarist, having worked together since 2002, combine their droll delivery in rhythmic, musically shaped phrases about dance and music, composition and space, audience and performer. Using scores by Morton Feldman (*Both Sitting*), or John Cage (*Cheap Lecture*) they create funny and fast-paced performances, part lecture, part critique, part stand-up comedy.

WILLIAM FORSYTHE
One Flat Thing, reproduced, *2002.*
Festspielhaus Hellerau, Dresden.

An endlessly inventive choreographer while director of
the Frankfurt Ballet, Forsythe subsequently formed his own
company and turned to rethinking the classical idiom. The
Forsythe Company has developed a rigorous and expanded
form of dance education to build entirely new bodies of
expertise. Dancers use supreme levels of physical and mental
strength to push through avant-garde ideas about dance,
space and the body. *One Flat Thing, reproduced* is performed
by fourteen dancers on and around twenty metal tables. The
dancers begin by pushing these in unison in a rush of air
downstage, and proceed to dance through and over them at
the highest imaginable speed. This is the kind of work that
only those with Forsythe's extreme ballet training could
devise and execute.

BORIS CHARMATZ

ABOVE Musée de la danse: Enfant, *2014.*
Sadler's Wells, London.
RIGHT Musée de la danse: Expo Zéro, *2011.*
Performa hub, New York.

Charmatz's *Musée de la danse* changes perceptions about dance as much as about museum display. It calls on viewers to consider the dancer's body as a container for the history of dance, its forms and its techniques, and to recognize that muscle memory is shaped by endless quotation from 20th-century choreography. *Expo Zéro*, an early 'exhibition' of Charmatz' *Musée*, was made up of gestural conversations between artists, dancers, philosophers, theorists and curators. Several complex 'exhibitions' later, Enfant examined the vexed issue of 'touch' with regard to children. Children in the performance are at first passive and limp, but soon take control, goading the adults into fiercely energetic movements. Bagpipes play at full blast as the children completely change the power dynamics of the stage.

FLUCT
Upward Facing Control Table Tops, *2017.*
Performa with Studio 94, Lever House, New York.
Photos by Paula Court.

Interrogating gender expression and bodily form through physically intense, fluid performances drawing on elements of techno music, the collaborative duo FlucT staged this one-night, dynamic conversation between movement and visual art. In a glass-walled, midtown skyscraper, eighteen dancers perform throughout the building's sterile office space – each floor is filled with sculptures, furniture and installations that the dancers play with, touch and straddle. Through raw, aggressive, sculptural motions – lifting and bending one another, marching across the cement rooms – the dancers command the gallery, disrupting any separation between art and live human form.

CHRISTIAN RIZZO

b.c., janvier 1545, 2007.
Commission for Festival Montepellier Danse.
Chai du Terral, Fontainebleau.

With characteristic minimalist motions and stripped set design, choreographer, fashion designer, rock musician and former opera director Christian Rizzo performed in and produced *b.c., janvier 1545* – an eerie, tense piece – with French dancer Julie Guibert. In a white-walled room, objects hang from the ceiling, silhouetted and unsettlingly corporeal – fraying, dripping forms. In stiletto heels Guibert moves around them in repetitive, angular motions as though her limbs are flattened, her body's contained forms referencing the 16th-century Cellini sculpture, *The Nymph of Fontainebleau*. Behind her, Rizzo wanders the space in a bizarre rabbit mask, slowly wheeling objects off-stage. Beating, haunting instrumentals by Gerome Nox suggested conflict, as suspense mounts between audience, dancer and voyeur. Tension grows yet there is no climax: the room empties leaving only Guibert onstage. The lights dim and leave her in blackness.

XAVIER LE ROY
Retrospective, *2012*.
Deichtorhallen, Hamburg.

This performance by Xavier Le Roy was a milestone
in being the first dance installation in a museum to use
the term 'retrospective' – more typical for an artist than
for a choreographer. The trajectory of Le Roy's career was
presented by dancers who not only performed works of his
spanning more than two decades, but also discussed them
with visitors who approached. In the traditional gallery sense,
the pieces were 'on view', although the configuration changed
every day and every hour, depending on the rotation of
dancers and their personal styles.

IVANA MÜLLER
While We Were Holding it Together, *2006.*
Poster/flyer for performance. Productiehuis, Rotterdam.

Croatian-born, Paris-based Müller looks to generate empathy between performers, creating situations that straddle both humour and discomfort. Five dancers take up the stage in a fixed tableau, immobile for 70 minutes, inviting audiences to affix their own narrative to each performer. Why is that woman reclining on the floor? Is that man with his arms outstretched holding something or releasing it? The dancers address the audience from time to time, each sentence beginning, 'I imagine', even as their breath becomes laboured and sweat runs down their brows from holding still throughout. Sounds of trains, helicopters and horses provide an intermittent soundtrack.

KEITH HENNESSY
Crotch *(all the Joseph Beuys references in the world cannot heal the pain, confusion, regret, cruelty, betrayal, or trauma...), 2009.*
Dance Theater Workshop, New York.
Photos by Yi-Chun Wu.

Hennessy's queer activism and DIY aesthetics, involving improvisation and occasionally forced audience participation, mix expressionistic gestures with political and spiritual content. Intentionally chaotic, motifs include poems read from torn notepaper, a manic lecture on German philosophy and dance, an athletic solo from a performer wearing a Halloween mask and an extended vignette of Hennessy weeping. The choreographer creates dances that hinge on his forceful persona, and an openness to expressing unlimited vulnerability.

MIGUEL GUTIERREZ
And Lose the Name of Action, *2012.*
Walker Art Center, Minneapolis.
Photo by Ian Douglas.

Often combining dance, drag, poetry, comedy and song, Gutierrez is a central force in a new generation of dance artists that use choreography to investigate emotion and cognitive experience. *And Lose the Name of Action* crafts a landscape of paranormal and hallucinatory movement, inspired in part by the artist's experience of his father undergoing operations to manage blood clots in the brain. Each moment maps a complex shift in the relationship between body and mind, offering access to an otherworldly logic of shifting moods.

NOÉMIE LAFRANCE
Agora II, *2006.*
McCarren Park Pool, Brooklyn, New York.
Photo by Bryan Thatcher.

Noémie Lafrance and her company, Sens Production, are known forlarge-scale dance performances that animate individual bodies in collective interventions that alter perceptions of public space. *Agora II* marked the reopening of a 5,100-square-metre (55,000 sq ft) pool that had been abandoned for twenty years in McCarren Park in Williamsburg, Brooklyn, and joined over seventy-five performers with thousands of viewers. The audience, who have been tasked with learning dance movements before their arrival, are instructed to play a 'choreographed game' of collective actions. *Agora II* became a vast social experiment, offering a narrative about the evolving community of Williamsburg. Audience members could not 'win' the game of competing actions, but rather had to solve the mystery of the collective together.

LA RIBOT

Panoramix, *1991–2003.*
Tate Modern, London.
Photo by Manuel Vason.

London-based Spanish artist La Ribot has built a
collection of 'Distinguished Pieces', short performances of
several minutes each, using 'readymades' – bed sheets, folding
chairs, a coat – as triggers for her expansive and quirky
movements. *Panoramix*, a retrospective, showed thirty-four
out of a total of one hundred pieces in which she transforms
her body into odd-shaped objects, and objects into curiously
animated figures. In line with the Fluxus-like actions of the
1960s and '70s, La Ribot brings a dancer's body-awareness and
stage presence to the Fluxus artists' fascination with chance
and indeterminacy.

NORA CHIPAUMIRE
Portrait of Myself as My Father, *2016.*
Photos by Elise Fitte-Duval and Gennadi Nash.

Zimbabwean-born, Brooklyn-based Chipaumire's body is steeped in the physicality of Southern African dance and movement. High kicks take off from deeply bent knees; arms extend at shoulder level; the body is weighted to the floor as it spins, leaps and drops. Confined in a boxing ring, this piece uses sport as a metaphor for male competitiveness and excellence. 'How do you become a black African man?' asks the artist through a microphone. Wearing athletic shoulder-pads, low-slung track pants and a tailcoat, three battle-dressed warriors (one Senegalese, one Zimbabwean and one Jamaican) viscerally attack stereotypes of the black male through an intertwined mix of movement vocabularies, drawing on tribal and contemporary dance as well as sports and the everyday.

MEG STUART
Auf den Tisch!, 2009.
Commission for Performa 09.
Baryshnikov Arts Center, New York.

American-born, Brussels-based
choreographer Meg Stuart devised *Auf den
Tisch!* (At the Table!), a literal platform for
a diverse group of performers, improvisers,
thinkers and writers, to talk to each other
about pressing issues – whether politics,
history or dance improvisation itself –
among a public who were encouraged to
join in if so moved. With one microphone
along each side of an expanded table
(made up of forty-nine small tables pushed
together), performers can start or end a
sentence or an action on the table, whenever
they choose. The inherent theatricality
of the unusual staging, the understanding
between performers of the give-and-take of
improvisation, as well as the easy integration
of movement and conversation are classic
features of Stuart's oeuvre.

FAUSTIN LINYEKULA
More, more, more...Future, *2010.*
Commission for Festival TransAmériques, Montreal.

Storyteller, choreographer, dancer and activist, Linyekula grew up in Kisangani in Zaire (now the Democratic Republic of Congo), under the repressive regime of dictator Mobutu Sese Seko. In 2001 he formed Studio Kabako, a multidisciplinary company-as-laboratory in the Congo that also engages in local initiatives. In a context where dance is a common social language for ritual, celebration, community and resistance, Linyekula's choreography is a container for muscle memories of decades of war, trauma and poverty that translates at international dance festivals into a profound humanism questioning the responsibility of audiences living far from such deprivation and horror.

WILL RAWLS
I make me [sic], *2016*.
Commission for Greater New York, MoMA PS1, Queens, New York.
Photo by Charles Roussel.

Will Rawls' oeuvre includes a roster of movements and shapes accumulated over almost two decades from notable choreographers and artists with whom he has worked, from Shen Wei to Marina Abramović, Tino Sehgal, Jérôme Bel, Alain Buffard, Noémie Lafrance and Yvonne Rainer. In *I make me [sic]*, the choreographer's own idiosyncratic style comes to the fore, showing a whole new level of expertise. Cultural history, the body as material and an elegant sense of space coalesce in a collage of dance, sound and personal anecdote. Starting with the letter 'A' and ending with the self-identifier 'I', evoked through text and movement, Rawls creates a personal index of choreographic forms for future development.

TACITA DEAN
Craneway Event, 2009.
Film still. Craneway Pavilion, Richmond, California.

Tacita Dean is known for her quiet, visually captivating films that function as a kind of cinematic portraiture. *Craneway Event* follows avant-garde choreographer Merce Cunningham and his company as they rehearse a new piece – one of his last – in an abandoned Ford factory. Overlooking the San Francisco Bay, the industrial space is immersed in light, the dancers silhouettes against the horizon. As is typical of Cunningham's process, the dancers rehearse without music, with architecture and nature complementing their form. Observing both the company and the late choreographer himself, the film is a soft, breathtaking meditation on movement and an icon's process.

SHARON LOCKHART
Five Dances and Nine Wall Carpets by Noa Ekshol, *2011.*
Film stills from five-channel installation.
Los Angeles County Museum of Art.

Researching and documenting overlooked communities and labourers – among them female clam diggers, a girls basketball team and industrial workers on lunch break – photographer and filmmaker Sharon Lockhart conceptualizes a theoretical conversation between herself and the late iconic Israeli choreographer Noa Eshkol, most known for developing a notation system that defines corporeal movement through a series of numbers and symbols. The choreography in this installation is precisely calibrated. The dancers move through calm, angular forms to a ticking metronome, as behind them stand vibrant, geometric 'wall rugs' made by the artist. The installation pays tribute to the late choreographer in a study of both the artist and her revolutionary form.

PINA BAUSCH
Vollmond, *2006.*
Schauspielhaus Wuppertal.

From Bausch's late repertoire, *Vollmond* is mellower
than her earlier portrayals of fraught relationships between
men and women. It is also more acrobatic, with powerful
male dancers taking the lead. A dark pool of water holds
centre stage, through which dancers race creating dramatic
arcs of spray as pouring rain drenches their unstoppable
motion. Designed by Peter Pabst, Bausch's exhilarating
spectacle of human energy mixed with nature's essence
maintains the vivid symbolism for which Bausch's classic
dance theatre is known.

CECILIA BENGOLEA &
FRANÇOIS CHAIGNAUD

Sylphides, 2008. Centre Pompidou, Paris.
Photos by Alain Monot.

Collaborating since 2005, Argentinian-born Bengolea, whose material could be described as a form of dance anthropology, and Paris-based Chaignaud, choreographer and dance historian, produce works that traverse ballet, voguing, twerking, Jamaican dancehall, hula hooping and clubbing. *Sylphides*, an homage to classical ballet but also a modern birth-and-death ritual, involves two performers encased in skin-tight latex bags, breathing through slim tubes.

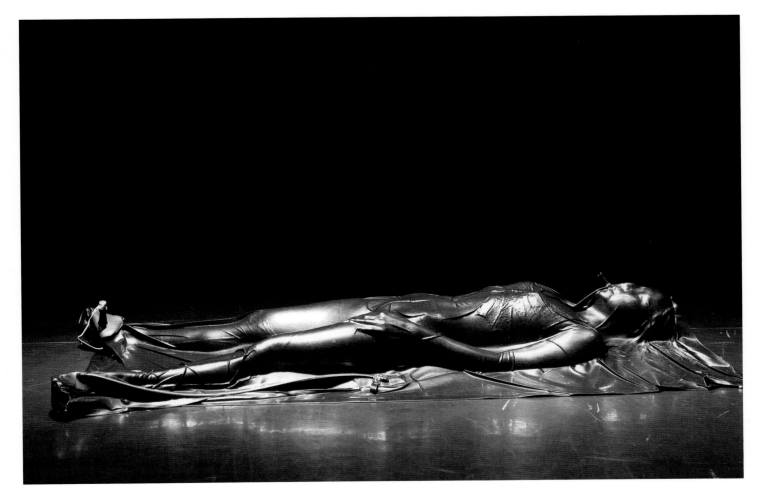

YVONNE RAINER

The Concept of Dust, or How do you look when there's nothing left to move?, *2014.*
Commissioned by the J. Paul Getty Museum,
Getty Research Institute and Performa,
Museum of Modern Art, New York.
Photos by Julieta Cervantes.

Seminal Judson Dance Theater figure Yvonne Rainer returned to dance in 2000 after twenty-five years, when Mikhail Baryshnikov invited her to work with him on the White Oak Dance project. Since then, she has taught and re-performed many key works including *Continuous Project Altered Daily*, 1969, and assembled an informal company, the Raindears, whose performances are faithful to her radical origins. Using a mélange of sports and dance references, philosophical and political quotations, her latest work, *The Concept of Dust*, is a powerful meditation on ageing interwoven with geopolitical considerations of the Middle East, based in literature and palaeontological findings.

SARAH MICHELSON
Devotion Study #1 – The American Dancer, *2012.*
Whitney Museum of American Art, New York.
Photo by Paula Court.

Focusing on her performance spaces has always been key to Michelson's work. Her ideas spiral from a given location, infecting the entire area – floor, walls, ceiling and atmosphere – with layered meaning for fiercely paced dancers to slice through. *In Devotion Study #1 – The American Dancer*, the fourth floor of Marcel Breuer's Whitney Museum was covered with a blueprint of the original floor plan, while the geometry of Breuer's cut-out window onto Madison Avenue provided a sharp counterpoint to a large green neon portrait of Michelson hanging on the opposite wall, as if overseeing the action. Six powerful dancers, relentlessly stepping backwards in circles for almost 90 minutes, fill the space with their precision movements, while Michelson designs and directs all the other parts – sound, lighting and costumes – and provides a live voiceover, in conversation with playwright Richard Maxwell, about history, religion and devotion to dance.

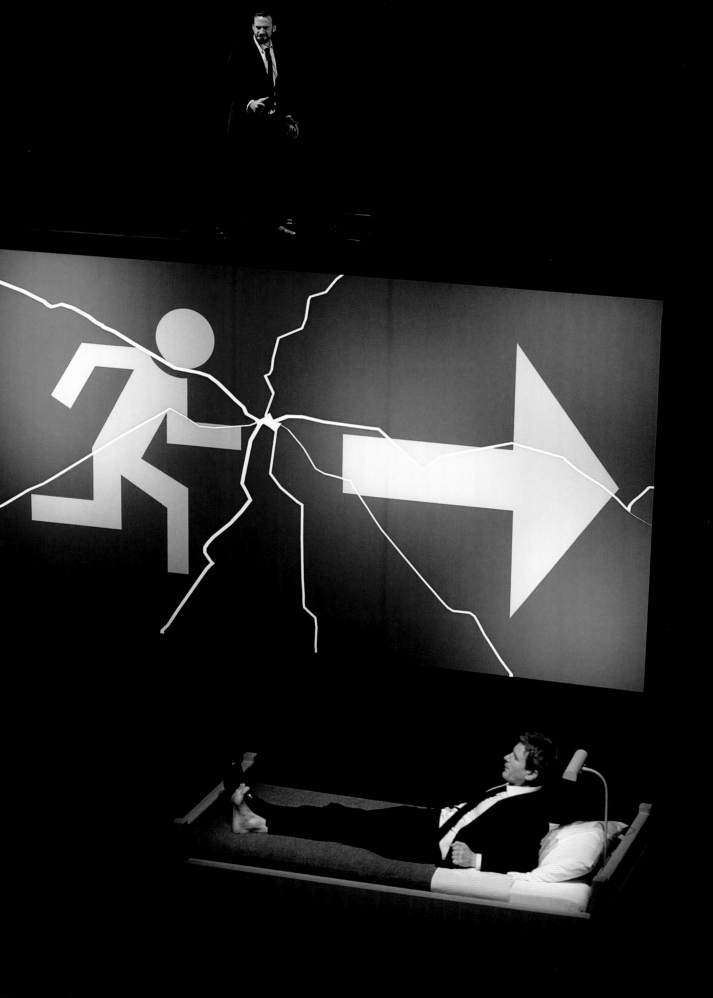

CHAPTER 5

Off Stage: New Theatre

ELMGREEN AND DRAGSET
Happy Days in the Art World, *2011.*
Commission for Performa 11, Skirball
Center for the Performing Arts, New York.
Photo by Paula Court.

In the mid-2000s, several productions that had all the markings of theatre – a script, actors, a director – began to be shown in museums and galleries, deconstructed so that all traditional 'theatre' elements, including backstage, might be exposed and exhibited. At the same time, several visual artists were taking to the stage. These artists made use of proscenium, curtains and wings, and took into account the fact that audience members would be seated in rows, viewing the work frontally. Yet seeing the two forms' 'trade tools', as it were, shifting contexts and expectations, served above all to underline their differences. Theatre performed by trained actors and directors proved quite distinct from performance by visual artists in just about every aspect of expertise, vision and intent.

The extent to which the differences between these types of performance serve to define them goes a long way towards illuminating the nature of performance art, the more paradoxical of the two. A visual art performance is most often the vision of a single artist, responsible for every element of the work. The artist is director, playwright, performer and lighting, costume and set designer rolled into one. The work rarely contains text or spoken word, often has no narrative arc, and is not required to 'make sense' in the way that theatre productions are frequently expected to resolve character relationships and plot by a play's end. More abstract than literal, performance by visual artists draws on the trajectory of art history, and its references are frequently to the aesthetic sensibilities of the times and to other artists. Such work is often highly personal; the artist might even be described as 'performing the self', their personal signature being very much the essence of the work.

Theatre more often than not begins with a script – with spoken lines and stage directions for the actors – including descriptions of the time and location of each scene change. It is made by a team effort of professionals, each with distinct functions – playwright, director, actor, producer, dramaturge, set designer, costume designer, lighting designer – and, because it involves many parts, typically takes longer to realize than does performance by a single visual artist. By the time a theatre production premiers, the highly personal vision of the playwright might be many times removed. Even so, the performers, who are the most visible manifestation of the entire enterprise, are reassured by the team effort and the clear demands of their profession. Their activity is acting, and they work to perfect the techniques of their métier, providing, with each play, a seamless rendering of the combined values and ideas of themselves, the playwright and the director.

The professionalism expected of the theatre actor – modulated voice, precise enunciation, solid stage presence and capability of projecting into large theatrical halls – becomes somewhat irrelevant in the visual art world, which disregards the accepted standards of theatrical etiquette and design. Actors predominantly work on the basis that an audience will pay attention to their delivery, comprehend the meaning of their words, and grasp the significance from start to finish of a tale well told. In the art world, the performer communicates very differently with his or her audience. In this context, the work is assembled in the manner of a collage or drawing, layered with image, sound or words combining eventually, if not at first, to suggest meaning. Without expecting to take away anything conclusive, art audiences have a greater role in completing the work for themselves, whether in the process of viewing or just as often, afterwards.

The freedom to create a performance with the immediacy of the lone artist working in a studio was enjoyed prolifically in the downtown New York avant-garde art community of the 1970s. Performers could play themselves, were encouraged to take off in any number of untried directions and to pursue ideas about the body as an object in space and time. This

flexibility and experimentation with a broad range of materials, crossing new music with dance, film and conceptual art, would come to influence many emerging playwrights and directors in Europe. Such figures recognized in this way of working the promise of a self-directed theatre, and material that probed and deconstructed the essence of their chosen medium when reduced to its basic elements. American directors and performers, including Meredith Monk, Robert Wilson, Elizabeth LeCompte, Richard Foreman, Laurie Anderson, Spalding Gray, Eric Bogosian and Karen Finley, many of whom toured widely in Europe, were understood to represent a new kind of performance that could exist on the boundary between visual art and theatre. Young European directors, equally influenced by European avant-garde theatre, took the freely idiosyncratic and inventive styles of the Americans' highly personalized performance-theatre as licence to create works of their own that stood outside of theatre history. Directors in the 1980s and '90s, in Germany, Belgium, France, the United Kingdom, Spain, Canada and Switzerland, including Jan Fabre, Jan Lauwers, Christoph Marthaler, Heiner Goebbels, La Fura dels Baus, Forced Entertainment, Gob Squad, Robert Lepage, Christoph Schlingensief and many more, created a landscape of intensely visual theatre and distinctive performance styles that were highly imaginative in their mixing of politics, literature, history and music. Their work was sometimes described under the heading 'post-dramatic theatre' for the ways in which traditional expectations were disrupted or abandoned entirely as conservative and oppressive to the imagination. Constructed with new media of all sorts and ingenious staging devices, these bold and compelling *Gesamtkunstwerk* of the late 1990s could be seen at theatre festivals from Avignon to Berlin, Paris, Brussels or Vienna.

Berlin-based Christoph Schlingensief's career provides a prime example of a personality-driven thinker moving reflexively across disciplines, from his appearances on film as a child actor, to his work as performer, film director, theatre director, opera director, TV talk-show host and politician from the late 1980s, to his visual art from the early 2000s. Taking elements from each discipline as needed, Schlingensief articulated the shifting cultural and political sands in a Berlin rapidly emerging from its isolation as a divided city, as well as a personal worldview that was as existentially complex as it was surreal. Confronting history, whether the horrors of the Third Reich – one film was titled *One Hundred Years of Adolf Hitler*

ELEVATOR REPAIR SERVICE
Gatz, 2006.
The Public Theater, New York.
Photo by Paula Court.

– homelessness and immigration, or society's obsessions with celebrity, including a disturbing 'happening' based on the death of Princess Diana, Schlingensief's productions, part vaudeville, part punk concert, disturbed audiences with their chaotic, satirical and hysterical renderings. Drawing on a concoction of references – from Luis Buñuel to radical German cinema of the 1960s and '70s, Joseph Beuys, the Viennese Actionists and Richard Wagner – Schlingensief's manic and unstoppable energy took final shape in his most ambitious project, an 'Opera Village' in Burkina Faso. This was an artistic space for cultural encounters and exchange, to which he applied the fierce humanism at the heart of his brazen and provocative drive. A school, a hospital, an opera house and a community would live on there after his death in 2010 from cancer at age forty-nine. Honoured with a posthumous 'retrospective' in the German Pavilion at the Venice Biennial the following year, Schlingensief would win the Golden Lion award for best national pavilion – recognition from the art world that lent a new perspective on his earlier material.

While Schlingensief directed his explosive imagination at all media – spilling out of the theatre onto the streets, disrupting the container of cinema, heaping everything together on an opera stage or co-opting the bandwidth of television to reach the mainstream – theatre director Frank Castorf, long-time artistic director of the Volksbühne in Berlin from 1992 to 2016, turned his incisive focus on theatre itself, creating volatile productions that would set the stage throughout the 1990s for an extraordinarily inventive and violently radical generation of theatre directors. With an innovative approach to showing live and mediated material simultaneously on stage, his work included brash deconstructions of classical plays and literature as well as wildly provocative 5-hour staged rampages involving nudity, drunkenness, thrown food, bad jokes and screaming at the audience. Presenting works by Christoph Marthaler, René Pollesch and Schlingensief, among others, as well as his own, the Volksbühne under Castorf's directorship would win multiple 'Theatre of the Year' accolades across Germany, and Castorf acquired a reputation as one of the most innovative stage directors of his time. Born and raised in East Germany, Castorf brought to theatre the inescapable watchfulness of someone having lived under a police state, and a belief in the stage as the ultimate public forum for critiquing the realities of a society in dangerous flux. Theatre for Castorf was a thought-carrier for powerful, expressionistic content – politics, philosophy, poetry – as well as an irresistible spectacle through which to evoke the day-to-day. Extending the legacy of the great German theatre pioneers – Erwin Piscator's scenographic inventions of the 1920s, Bertolt Brecht's epic plays and influential theories about audience intervention and confrontation and Heiner Müller's poetic, deconstructivist approach to text and authorship – he introduced his own obsession with crossing theatre and cinema, producing a hybrid that he believed could not be achieved by one or the other medium alone. Embedded cameras revealed parts of the stage, hallways, balconies and tangential spaces that audiences could not see; large projected headshots showed close-ups of actors' fleeting expressions and emotions. Indeed, Castorf's marathon productions with their varied directorial approaches, opinionated cast of regular actors, and frenetic play on the margins between rock and roll, popular culture and visual art (Jonathon Meese created the sets for one of his plays) were a

YOUNG JEAN LEE
The Shipment, 2009.
The Kitchen, New York.
Photo by Paula Court.

call for a theatre of meaning – proud advertisements for the power of the art of the stage to get under peoples' skin and to change their minds.

Such boisterous combinations were particular to post-unification Berlin theatre, where politics and art, East and West, capitalism and old-style communism, and the visible discrepancies between these – on people's faces, in their clothing and on disintegrating building facades – were an inescapable part of everyday reality. Disruptive and aggressive, this material was evidence of the trauma of separation, and of an inescapably slow recovery. In France, performances by Philippe Quesne or Gisèle Vienne conjured a very different mindscape. These were sophisticated reimaginings of the day-to-day, of history and philosophy, and of society with a futuristic lean. Achieving an aesthetics of extreme elegance, such cinematic, slow-motion chimeras of indelible image-making are also eerily disconcerting, punctuated with quiet charges of social or political critique. Quesne, who studied visual art and graphic design; who works across a spectrum of disciplines and exhibition spaces from galleries to urban parks, inside and outside of theatre; and who writes and directs his own plays, produces subtle theatrical works of few words that offer rich commentary on society nevertheless. With actors, dancers, artists and musicians making up his collaborative performance laboratory, Vivarium, he creates

sets of unexpected wonder: a rec room where characters play a game of table tennis morphs into a snowy back yard; a forest becomes a metal-themed amusement park built by a band of rock-and-rollers with inflatable sculptures. His close studies of human beings in an imaginatively reconfigured daily life are just as often presented under dance as under theatre banners, as though the distinction between the two did not apply here or, rather, suggesting that concentrating on narratives of bodies moving in space can be understood as a melding of both. Similarly, Vienne's productions, which since 2004 have been written in collaboration with American author Dennis Cooper, are seen in both dance and theatre camps. Working with professional dancers and trained actors, the artist considers each as an object in space to be moved, with dancers playing out the underlying rhythm of a work and actors signalling its psychological threads. Life-sized puppets interact with live performers, robotic figures wearing oversized pagan-like costumes move to the sounds of a black metal band on stage, and layers of scrims and film projections combine to create narratives of heightened anxiety, including ghost stories and serial murders. Vienne's uncanny ceremonies are designed to have each part – image, sound, bodies, text – pull at the seams between dream and reality.

In New York, the early 2000s saw an entirely different sensibility emerge with a new generation of theatre artists. On the one hand, a do-it-yourself aesthetic was the hallmark of several collectives such as Big Art Group, Radiohole and Hoi Polloi. Rough and chaotic, and more intimate in scale than the work of the previous decade, their found-object quality had as much to do with the economics of maintaining a theatre company amid the rising values of downtown real estate as with the ethos and preoccupations of a generation inured to spectacle – an attitude they shared with their audiences. Many located across the East River to Brooklyn to find affordable live-and-work spaces where lofts and basements had, initially at least, the feel of 1970s SoHo. Extending the downtown region to include Williamsburg, Bushwick and Astoria in Queens, venues for this generation of theatre artists included The Kitchen, Performance Space 122, Abrons Arts Center, Here and Dixon Place, as well as Issue Project Room, Chocolate Factory, Roulette, Jack and the Collapsable Giraffe that made use of available spaces in old industrial buildings.

Another group of downtown playwrights and directors were analytical in their approach to parsing the elements of theatre – words, bodies, audience – and used as their springboard seminal figures of the 1970s and '80s avant-garde such as Richard Foreman (with his simultaneous presentation of texts and voiceovers that deconstructed his intentions and the meaning of his words even as actors spoke them) and Elizabeth LeCompte and the Wooster Group (with their breakdown of theatre time into modules of history, classic texts, pop culture, everyday life and technology low and high). Elevator Repair Service, Nature Theater of Oklahoma, Richard Maxwell and his New York City Players and playwright and director Young Jean Lee each produced highly original material that by the end of the first decade of the 2000s constituted a new kind of downtown theatre: sparse, intellectual, unfettered by media or staging devices, yet clever in its transparent questioning of the 'thing itself' – theatre. Each company developed its own method for making plays. Elevator Repair Service built their scripts collaboratively from well-known novels over a period of eighteen months or more; Nature Theater created (as in their most recent work) a durational play whose script was a word-for-word transcription (pauses for breath and 'ums' included) of a woman recording her life story from childhood to the present. Each used material of their own making, focusing on transforming a textual artwork into a theatrical one.

How to speak, what to say, how to act without acting, how to be in conversation with each member of the audience and how to do all of the above without resorting to technology or special effects – these were the basic building blocks that each company used in different configurations. Not surprisingly, this stripped-down approach to theatre and its conceptual guide rails appealed to artists and art critics who took note of its similarities to the theory of 'relational aesthetics' that made connections between viewer, object, surrounding space and the combination of these, suggesting a kind of multi-dimensional theatre of the self. Richard Maxwell's *Untitled*, 2012, at the Whitney Museum of American Art demonstrated just such an amalgamation of ideas. Presented in a large floor-through gallery in the museum as part of a week-long residency, it made all aspects of the creative process visible, showcasing the mechanisms of theatre, its silences and stillnesses, as well as the coming and going of visitors. 'Playwright and director Richard Maxwell will make theater in the Museum, reframing rehearsal as an open and publicly presented activity,' announced the museum's press release. Maxwell and his theatre company

rehearsed his new play from 11 a.m. until 6 p.m. daily, with a lunch break from 2 until 2.45 p.m. The ideal viewer, Maxwell said, would stay for an entire day.

The specificity of circumstances of Maxwell's production was critical to his way of thinking about a theatre that might take audiences into new realms of self-reflection and understanding. Yet nothing in this vein could compare to Paul Chan's *Waiting for Godot*, staged in 2007 on the bleak streets of New Orleans, two years after the devastating tragedy of Hurricane Katrina had flooded over 80 per cent of the city, leaving thousands dead or homeless. The magnitude of Chan's achievement lies in the visual artist's expansive approach to relating a play about interminable waiting and desolation to a community's catastrophic desolation and interminable waiting for relief and repair. Using the comforting traditions of New Orleans – a gumbo dinner, a marching band – Chan had viewers follow signage nailed to several posts along the way, marked 'A Country Road. A Tree. Evening' (the opening words setting the scene in Samuel Beckett's script), to a street corner in the Lower Ninth Ward. Seamlessly transitioning from life into Beckett's play, the two-act tragicomedy seemed to have been written on the spot: 'What do you do when you fall far from help?', Vladimir asks. 'We wait till we can get up,' says Pozzo, 'And then we go on. On!' – words that brought clarity to a famously mystifying text. Perhaps it is only in the hands of a visual artist that such a work could have unfolded with so much space to insert personal imaginings, and with so many doors left ajar for viewers to step onto the borderless stage and become one of the *dramatis personae* themselves. Literal, but never in such a manner as to allow realism to overtake the delicate sensibilities of the players, or of the viewers who knew the story only too well from direct experience, Chan appropriated theatre with the licence to make of it whatever he could, which he did.

Using the stage as exhibition space, or the theatre and its textual and narrative traditions as materials to manipulate at will is the prerogative of the visual artist. It is expected of these artists to experiment and to surprise, to work without the safety net of tradition, and to take that step with the intention of venturing into untried territories, forcing fresh responses to the unfamiliar upon themselves. Such work is approached with the same care and sophistication that an artist might apply in other media, but above all with an exact understanding of their reasoning for choosing one medium over another.

BUILDERS ASSOCIATION
House/Divided, 2006.
The Public Theater, New York.
Photo by Paula Court.

Known for performances that capture the impact of
social phenomena engineered through technology – the rise
of call centres, identity theft or 'networked selves' occupying
multiple global locations – the Builders Association was
characteristically of-the-moment in depicting the nationwide
trauma generated by the mortgage foreclosure crisis in the
United States. Referencing John Steinbeck's *The Grapes of
Wrath* – a harrowing tale of dustbowl migration and poverty
following an earlier crash in America's history in 1929 – the
piece uses large screen projections to create a rich visual
landscape for an 80-minute drama of current affairs.

ELEVATOR REPAIR SERVICE
Gatz, 2006.
The Public Theater, New York.
Photo by Paula Court.

F. Scott Fitzgerald's rich and complex language served as the inspiration for this 6-hour-long performance of *The Great Gatsby*, which included every word of the 1925 text. While in traditional theatre plot, character and setting serve as structuring elements, language here becomes a driving force that is as integral to the action as it is to the book. The production invited the audience to imagine the action as if they were reading it themselves, with the cast of thirteen actors in a shabby office of a mysterious small business, instead of opulent 1920s Long Island. After a series of strange coincidences, it becomes clear that the book and its language are transforming the actors.

HOI POLLOI
All Hands, *2012.*
Incubator Arts Project, New York.
Photo by Ryan Jensen.

From 2010 until 2014, the Incubator Arts Project was a hub for some of the most exciting, risk-taking and off-the-radar new theatre work around. *All Hands* was one such production – a play about the eccentric characters, rituals and codes in the world of secret societies. Set in a drab carpeted conference room, it depicts a mysterious fictional cult whose purpose only becomes more undecipherable as the play progresses through non-narrative scenes. The participants are tracked from mundane moments of cleaning to highly choreographed ensemble dance numbers. As the performance becomes more abstract, the absurdist and theatrical qualities of the secret world offer reflection on the world of experimental theatre itself.

TAYLOR MAC

A 24-Decade History of Popular Music, *2011-17.*
St Ann's Warehouse, Brooklyn, New York.
Photo by Teddy Wolff.

This extravagant, 24-hour hybrid of drag, concert and history charts popular music in the United States from 1776 to the present. Through renditions of 246 original songs, Taylor Mac reflects on the country's social history, adorned in vibrant, carnivalesque costumes and accompanied by an opulent live band and helpers known as 'Dandy Minions'. Given mattresses to sleep on, periodic meals to maintain their energy, and invitations to join the interactive merriment, audience members become active participants in the marathon performance. Staged only once in its day-long form, this technicolour epic traced the powerful formation of gay communities over the past two centuries of a country's turbulent, and often-oppressive, political history.

RADIOHOLE
Fluke, 2006.
PS122, New York.
Photo by Lisa Whiteman.

Radiohole has created a hub for young theatre artists
in their garage in Bushwick, Brooklyn – the 'collapsible hole'
where they have collaboratively created spectacular visuals
and technologically savvy installations. In *Fluke*, the small
ensemble of four performed Herman Melville's *Moby-Dick*
with their eyes closed, and fish-like eyes painted on the back
of their eyelids, as they navigated and responded to a complex
Rube Goldberg-like set of oceanic ephemera. Throughout
the performance the audience witnessed an elaborate sensory
overload of enigmatic riffs on *Moby-Dick*, including gurgling
sounds of the deep ocean and quick light changes.

BIG ART GROUP

RIGHT Broke House, *2012.*
Abrons Arts Center, New York.
RIGHT BELOW Dead Set 3, *2007.*
The Kitchen, New York.

Both *Dead Set 3* and *Broke House* manifest
Big Art Group's signature style of using
new media and technology to challenge and
update theatrical forms. Using live video,
choreography, digital puppeteering and special
effects, *Dead Set* is a series of short theatrical
motifs that tackle the idea of trauma. These
conceptual motifs, such as 'colour therapy'
and 'real time film', are hybrids of video and
theatre in which actors embody a range of
psychotic states. *Broke House* takes place on a
set of video screens that capture actors in real
time as they try to recall their own relations
to family, architecture and their beliefs. Big
Art Group makes the audience active editors
of the work, as they must navigate multiple
screens, projections and audio environments.
Character, scene and story are manipulated
into a matrix that transforms liveness in the
digital and information age.

CARRIE MAE WEEMS
Grace Notes: Reflections for Now, *2016*.
Spoleto Festival, Charleston.
Photos by William Struhs.

Known for her poetic, intimate ability to celebrate
black beauty and explore daily life amid racial stereotype
and oppression, photographer, writer and filmmaker
Carrie Mae Weems wrote and performed in this elegy
to young black men murdered in acts of racial violence
in the contemporary United States. Through street
dance, opera and spoken word, the performance follows
a woman who, like a modern Antigone, must grapple
with her brothers' deaths and with those who deny them
a proper burial, all the while maintaining a sense of self
through unspeakable challenge. At the close of the piece,
videos play scene after scene of hand-held footage showing
young black men being killed – visceral images of the
tragedies that Weems writes into dramatic history.

RASHID JOHNSON
Dutchman, 2013.
Commission for Performa 13, Russian and Turkish Baths,
East Village, New York.
Photos by Paula Court.

Always elegant and impactful, Johnson's first live performance was a reimagining of *Dutchman*, an award-winning play written in 1964 by LeRoi Jones (later known as Amiri Baraka) at the height of the civil rights movement. A political allegory that wanders into the surreal, its presentation in the steam rooms of an old bathhouse instigates a journey through physical sensations and emotional atmospheres for actors and audiences alike. The extreme conditions disrupt the narrative flow of the play – a tense confrontation between a black man and a white woman on a subway train that continually teeters on violence – so that the drama unfolds in fits and starts, and explodes at the point when the unbearable heat and horrific end of the play coincide.

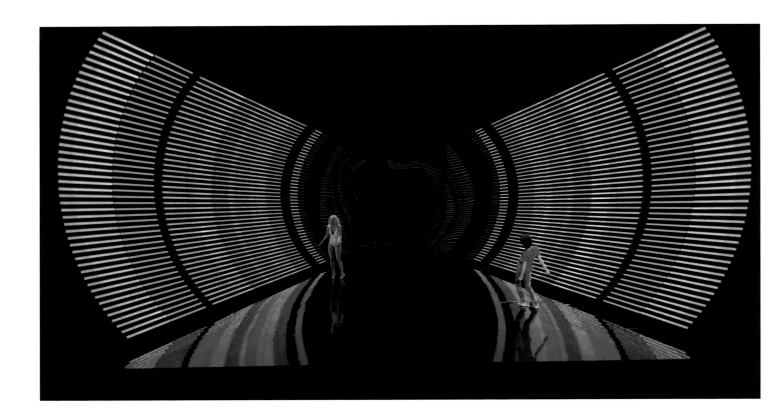

GISÈLE VIENNE
The Pyre, *2013.*
Centre Pompidou and IRCAM, Paris.
Photo by Hervé Veronese.

Merging dance, puppetry and multimedia collaboration through her performances, Gisèle Vienne choreographed this frantic, dystopian exploration of the tension between narration and abstraction. Beneath a spotlight, a woman jolts in contorted, unsettling motions, the stage around her dark except for curved walls that form a tunnel of flashing light. A young boy enters the stage, his relationship to the woman unclear. As he joins her and responds to her movement and form they appear trapped in the pulsating, otherworldly tunnel, confined as they struggle against reality and their predetermined narrative fate. At the end of the performance the audience is given the final act – a novella by Dennis Cooper, both to unsettle and to confirm interpretation.

ROBERT WILSON
Steve Buscemi, Actor, *2004.*
Still from video portrait.

In a series of life-sized 'video portraits', stage director extraordinaire Robert Wilson uses technology to capture the essence of his highly visual, and powerfully physical, directing signatures: stillness and stylized gesture and movement. Disguising the monitor as a large frame for a still photograph, Wilson creates high-definition portraits-on-a-loop of vital, breathing subjects, including a Sumo wrestler, artists, directors, actors, a snow owl and a black panther. Wilson's absolute focus is on looking-over-time; he shows what the eye sees, and specifically how it sees character in each individual outline. The subjects of his portraits, filmed over many hours for what will be edited down to studies of 3–12 minutes, are shown outside their 'natural habitat'. Wilson assigns roles and adds iconographic detail as would be expected of such a masterful director. In this portrait of actor Steve Buscemi, the moustachioed 'butcher' oversees a bloody carcass, motions of chewing serving as the give-away to the underlying live nature of the portrait.

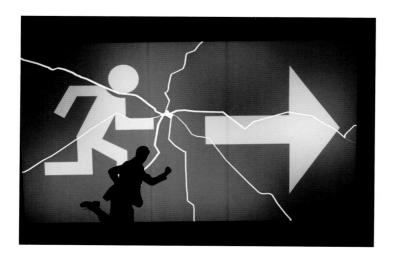

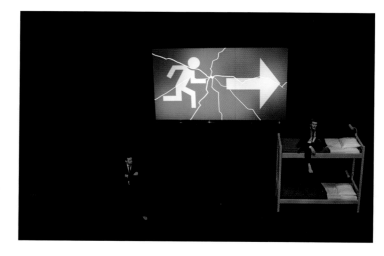

ELMGREEN AND DRAGSET
TOP AND LEFT Drama Queens, *2007.*
Municipal Theatre, Münster.
CENTRE Happy Days in the Art World, *2011.*
Commission for Performa 11, Skirball Center for the
Performing Arts, New York.
Photos by Paula Court.

Drama Queens presents superstars from the history of 20th-century sculpture in the form of scaled-down replicas. With individual actors providing personality and voice for each psychologically nuanced 'character', and remote-control operators sending each sculpture reeling as they argue and confront one another about their place in art history and the market, this institutional critique imagines museums late at night.

An intimate double self-portrait of the artists themselves, played by actors Joseph Fiennes and Charles Edwards, *Happy Days* uses the style of Beckett's invariably duelling partners to discuss the creative process of two artists presenting as one, and how such a twosome can maintain their inspired partnership following separation.

SIMON FUJIWARA

The Boy Who Cried Wolf, *2011.*
Commission for Performa 11, Abrons Arts Center, New York.
Photo by Paula Court.

In this richly detailed narrative set on a revolving stage, Fujiwara's childhood, family history, and life as an artist and human being are mined to create a series of engaging episodes that simultaneously sample excerpts from political and cultural history. An ingenious storyteller, the artist both excavates and concocts juicy histories and animates them with exaggeration and humour. Through the stories and anecdotes crafted by his assumed personae, he questions our notions of historical and collective memory and examines its malleability.

GOB SQUAD
Western Society, *2010*.
Promotional image, Hebbel am Ufer, Berlin.

Staging chaotic, lively performances that draw
inspiration from pop cultural artefacts, the artist collective
Gob Squad produced this absurdist, exuberant study of
perception in the digital age. In gold lamé outfits and
bleached, faux-California blonde wigs the actors assemble
around a mundane brown couch, recreating an obscure,
homemade YouTube video of a family gathering. A moveable
screen splits actors and live audience as the action is live-
streamed to a second set of viewers. As the scene progresses
the performance shifts between the playful and the critical.
Actors ask each other intimate, provocative 'either-or'
questions, and use the family scene to discuss their own
personal, difficult relationships as the play simultaneously
satirizes, mocks and expands the domestic space.

DAVID LEVINE
Habit, *2012.*
Installation view, Essex Street Market, New York.
Photo by Julieta Cervantes.

Blending the traditions of durational performance
art and theatrical production, David Levine's voyeuristic
90-minute play was performed by three actors continuously
for 8 hours a day over one week. Like an installation in an
art gallery, *Habit* was staged in the cavernous space of the
former Essex Street Market in a four-walled, fully furnished
and functional American ranch house (stocked refrigerator,
working stove, plumbing, running water), where audience
members could peer through open windows or move around
as they pleased. Although the language never changes, the
actors improvise the staging to suit their needs – when they're
hungry, they cook; when they're dirty, they wash. *Habit* fuses
conventional theatre, reality TV and visual arts performance,
short-circuiting our assumptions about spectatorship,
performance, routine, reality and realism.

MY BARBARIAN
Post-Living Ante-Action Theater, *2016*.
New Museum, New York.
Photo by Vanessa Cuervo.

New York- and Los Angeles-based performance collective My Barbarian appropriates standard theatrical styles of narrative, musical theatre and camp to inventively probe the politics of theatre and its potential as an instrument for radical enquiry. Inspired by previous activist theatre collectives, such as The Living Theater and Antiteater, Barbarian's *Post-Living Ante-Action Theater* gathered an international cast of artists, actors, scholars, comedians, dancers and musicians who met regularly over a period of eight years to develop workshops, performances and events for our times.

MARINA ROSENFELD
P. A. / HARD LOVE, *2009*.
Commission for Performa 09 with Park Avenue Armory, New York.
Photo by Paula Court.

Composer, sound artist, visual artist, experimental turntablist and performer, Rosenfeld's vocabulary is constructed from a complex integration of notation and improvisation. During an artist-in-residence programme at the Wade Thompson Drill Hall of the Park Avenue Armory, Rosenfeld utilized vintage public address speakers from sports stadiums to create a multi-directional sound installation within the vast space. Illuminated by tiny lamps, horns for each speaker present designate a performance area where pre-recorded electro-acoustic sound and vocals are also projected. Reciting brief scripts from select movies nearby, Rosenfeld is joined by cellist Okkyung Lee, whose playing expands on the pre-recorded sounds, focusing on pockets of reverberation both close up and far away.

CLAIRE FONTAINE
Situations, *2011*.
Film still.
Metro Pictures Gallery, New York.

'Claire Fontaine', the invention of a Paris-based feminist art collective (Fulvia Carnevale and James Thornhill) formed in 2004, whose name is taken from a brand of popular French notebooks and stationery, presents herself as a fictional readymade artist in the school of Marcel Duchamp. Her highly conceptual 'found objects' appropriate a broad range of styles from peer artists, critiquing art theory and the idea of originality as much as the economics and internal machinations of the art world. Fontaine's elegant and ironic exercises include *Situations* – a performance transferred to film by a company that specializes in self-help and promotional videos. Following Fontaine's script, the video instructs viewers in how to behave in a street fight. Three casually dressed male actors in a white cube space demonstrate a series of lessons in self-defence, including the use of knives and body slamming. Both found object and stylized performance, the video's clinical instructions make the work both unsettling and curiously entertaining.

RICHARD MAXWELL
The End of Reality, *2006.*
The Kitchen, New York.
Photo by Paula Court.

Through his company The New York City Players, founded
in 1996, Richard Maxwell has created a distinctive and sparse
theatrical style that strips language of emotion and delivers
characters with sterile and stiff precision. Set in the security
room of a nondescript building, *The End of Reality* stages a series
of conversations between security guards who rarely interact, and
who deliver long speeches that elicit feelings of apathy and despair.
Intermittently, comically clunky fight scenes occur between the
guards and criminals that highlight the banality of violence and
ordinary disaffection in everyday American life.

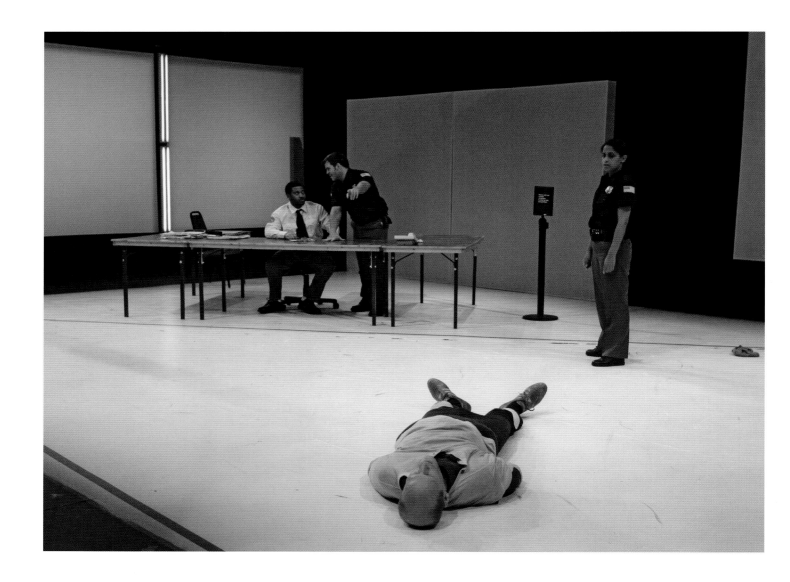

TOSHIKI OKADA
Freetime, 2008.
Live House Super Deluxe, Roppongi, Tokyo.
Photo by Tory Yokota.

Born in 1973 in Yokohama, Japan, playwright, director
and novelist Toshiki Okada gives voice to Japan's lost
generation of the *hikikomori* – a term to describe unemployed
twenty-five- to thirty-year-old recluses in the midst of Japan's
recession in the 1990s. *Freetime* is set in a Japanese diner
where the employees become interested in the writings
of a customer's personal journal. The customer visits the
diner every morning before work and ponders the nature
of her free time as a form of capitalistic labour. Okada leads
in contemporary dance theatre with his minimalistic set
designs and bountiful Japanese colloquialisms.

EDGAR ARCENEAUX
Until, Until, Until..., *2015.*
Commission for Performa 15, New York.
Photo by Paula Court.

Known for splicing scrims and projection screens in elegant
installations, Arceneaux's first live performance was an homage
to vaudevillian Bert Williams – America's first mainstream black
entertainer active from the 1890s to the 1920s – and to Hollywood
star Ben Vereen, whose appearance as Williams wearing 'black face'
at Ronald Reagan's inaugural ball in 1981 badly backfired when his
critical explanation as to why he did so was cut from the broadcast.
Until, Until, Until..., based on the footage that never aired that night,
was presented in a layered mise-en-scène that included clips from the
inaugural party, with live performers representing Ben Vereen and
'Donny and Marie', who also performed on that fateful night. The
piece questions the truth of muddled narratives from the past, and
goes some way towards restoring Vereen in the present.

FRANK CASTORF
Meine Schneekönigin, *2004.*
Volksbühne, Berlin.

Artistic director of Berlin's famed Volksbühne, Castorf
dismantles Hans Christian Andersen's *The Snow Queen,*
throwing players together on a set that involves storms of
fake snow, broken mirrors and roaming Nazi soldiers among
other violently cast debris. In this 3-hour adaption, Castorf
draws from his arsenal of theatrical disturbances, built over a
long and provocative theatre career, including 'flying potato
salad, inserted theoretical texts, urinating in a zinc bucket,
booming music, film projections, hysterical family life, nude
madness, improvised speeches and plenty of slapstick'.

LUCIANO CHESSA
Music for 16 Futurist Noise Intoners, *2009.*
Commission for Performa 09, Town Hall, New York.
Photos by Paula Court.

For the 100th anniversary of the founding of Futurism, sound artist and futurist composer Luciano Chessa reconstructed sixteen intonarumori – crank-operated instruments originally designed by avant-garde musician Luigi and destroyed in the early 20th century. The inner mechanics of the instruments are hidden inside bulky wooden crates, funnel-shaped speakers producing fantastical grinding, churning noises for the orchestra's original and newly commissioned compositions. Live vocalizations accompany select movements, while others solely use the shrieks, bellows and clicks of the historic instruments in an exploration of machine-as-sound.

ANT HAMPTON & TIM ETCHELLS
The Quiet Volume, *2010.*
Reading room of the Universitätsbibliothek der Humboldt, Berlin.

The Quiet Volume, a collaboration between two acclaimed British theatre artists of different generations, is a play set in a library that exploits the tension common to any such setting – a combination of silence and concentration within which different people's experiences of reading unfold. Two audience members sit side-by-side taking cues from words both written and whispered. Exposing us to the strange magic at the heart of the reading experience, the process allows aspects of reading that we think of as deeply internal to leak out into the surrounding space, from one reader's sphere into another's.

FRANCES STARK
Put a Song in Your Thing, *2011.*
Commission for Performa 11, Abrons Arts Center, New York.
Photo by Paula Court.

Language, its rhythm and its poetry are central to
Frances Stark's engagement with the world. Borrowing
words and phrases from novels, poems and pop songs, she
turns them into visual materials that evoke the process
of writing. *Put a Song in Your Thing* is a semi-autobiographical
stroll through the creative chaos of the artist's life. The piece
features dancer, DJ and Major Lazer 'hype man' Skerrit
Bwoy, as well as artist Mark Leckey's BigBox sound system.

LIZ MAGIC LASER
I Feel Your Pain, *2011.*
Commission for Performa 11, SVA Theater, New York.
Photo by Paula Court.

This mixed-media performance restaged America's recent
political contests as a romantic drama. Drawing on a variety of
agit-prop theatre tactics, particularly the Russian constructivist
idea of a 'living newspaper', *I Feel Your Pain* examined how emotion
is used to establish authenticity on America's political stage. Staged
in a movie theatre, the performance took place simultaneously in
the midst of the audience and on the cinema's screen. Eight actors
perform a sequence of scenes that trace the progression of a romantic
relationship in adapted dialogues taken from political interviews
and press conferences with Sarah Palin and Glenn Beck, among
others. As the actors perform, live film from two cinematographers
in the audience is projected onto the screen as a continuous feed,
with Laser acting as a real-time editor, seated at monitors in the
projection booth choosing camera angles for the audience to see.

PHILIPPE QUESNE

La Mélancolie des Dragons, *2010.*
La Paraffe au Théâtre, Avignon.

Six heavy-metal musicians are sitting in a stalled car
listening to vintage 1980s tunes. Stranded in the middle of
a snowy forest, they will spend the rest of the production
deciding on how to construct an amusement park there
with the help of an elderly woman. Throughout this surreal
adventure, Quesne mixes dream and reality, music and
language, in a visually arresting style, stemming from his
work as a visual artist, to contrast atmospheres of mystery
and magic with moments of mundanity and awkwardness.

DIMITRIS PAPAIOANNOU

LEFT Nowhere, *2009*.
Greek National Theatre, Athens.
LEFT BELOW Primal Matter, *2012*.
Hellenic Festival, Athens.

Trained as a painter, Greek theatre director Dimitris Papaioannou makes large-scale spectacles with an obsessive attention to visual detail, paying close attention to the seduction and presence of the human body, its gestures and its emotional potential. In *Nowhere*, he explores the nature of the theatrical stage as a surface and spatial mechanism that is continually transformed and redefined by human presence. Twenty-six performers move, measure and mark out a large mechanical structure of pulleys and levers on the stage using their bodies, pitting themselves against a highly complex machine of considerable dimensions and technical capabilities. In *Primal Matter* the artist performs with a nude male dancer in sequences that explore relationships between the primitive and the modern, identity and otherness. The austerity of the performance, which features a series of choreographic illusions that include the dancers appearing to dismember their own limbs using fabric and props, reflects the devastating cultural and economic shifts occurring in the choreographer's home country of Greece.

LAGARTIJAS TIRADAS AL SOL

El Rumor del Incendio, *2010*.
Universidad Nacional Autónoma de México.

El Rumor del Incendio blends witness accounts, archive film and scale models as actors unearth artefacts from the violent history of revolutionary student uprisings in 1960s Mexico. Coming of age in the aftermath of a period of a thousand disappearances and an unknown number of deaths that resulted from these movements, Lagartijas Tiradas al Sol was founded by a generation of artists who have used theatrical devices to give life and voice to overlooked moments in their social and political histories. This documentary play reignites the shadowed histories of the guerrilleros of a previous generation, and in particular the personal experiences of one woman, Margarita Urías, to uncover the utopian tendencies of that period, linking them to present-day political projects in Mexico.

DAN GRAHAM
Don't Trust Anyone Over Thirty, *2004.*
Walker Art Center, Minneapolis.

Celebrated for his reflective, perception-distorting mirror and glass pavilions and his documentary analyses that fuse rock music and cultural critique, Dan Graham created this exuberant, absurd rock opera, starring ten marionettes and the punk band Japanther, as a trippy satire of the 1960s hippie generation. The narrative follows young rocker Neil Sky, who becomes a presidential candidate and wins. Comedic chaos ensues, as his first major law sends all citizens over the age of thirty to LSD-centric re-education centres. Featuring puppet sex, rock and roll interjections, and hallucinogenic visuals, this is a story of youth culture, idealism and political revolution in a psychedelic haze.

HANS ULRICH OBRIST & PHILIPPE PARRENO
Il Tempo Del Postino, *2009.*
Opera House, Manchester.
Photo by Hugo Glendinning.

This dynamic hybrid of exhibition, opera and live performance gave acclaimed visual artists (here Matthew Barney) 15-minute slots to present a piece in any medium besides film or video. The diverse performances included a cattle-bidding among the audience, opera singers moving through the aisles singing *Madame Butterfly,* and a live orchestra playing back any sound made in the crowd, producing a radical, spontaneous reimagining of the presentation and reception of visual arts.

PAPPA TARAHUMARA
Ship in a View, *2012.*
Theatre Senju, Tokyo.
Photo by Hiroshi Koike.

Pappa Tarahumara is a Japanese dance-theatre troupe
directed by Hiroshi Koike that merges the ominous qualities
of Japanese Noh theatre with modern dance. In *Ship in a View,*
rhythmic chants of a forgotten religion and dancers' slow
emotive movements draw out a supernatural depiction of
a nation's dreams, or perhaps nightmares. The imaginative
series presents dreams in a ceremonial framework that
suggests an ongoing communication between the conscious
and subconscious mind. A flagpole stands erect as a place
marker for reality, yet even then it vacillates as a pole on
a playground or a pole on a ship. The performance revisits
scenes of Japan's recent history as memories, rendering
visible the mental negotiations of daydreamers as parts of
an unfolding narrative.

NATURE THEATER OF OKLAHOMA
Romeo and Juliet, *2008.*
The Kitchen, New York.
Photo by Peter Nigrini.

Romeo and Juliet retells Shakespeare's classic love story with nearly verbatim language transcribed from phone interviews with eight people, who were asked to recount the play in their own words. The result was a hilarious mishmash of half-recalled quotes, mixed-up plots and wild digressions performed in traditional Shakespearean style with all the trappings that audiences associate with Shakespeare: a proscenium arch, frilly costumes, two star-crossed lovers over-enunciating every line. This was Nature Theater of Oklahoma's break-out production for using overheard speech as a tool of theatrical manipulation, as well as a way to extend a play's authorship into the outside world.

THE WOOSTER GROUP
TO YOU, THE BIRDIE! (Phèdre), *2000.*
The Performing Garage, New York.
Photo by Paula Court.

Formed in 1975 in Soho, New York, The Wooster Group reimagines the canonical 1677 French play, *Phèdre* by Jean Racine in the exhilarating performance, *TO YOU, THE BIRDIE!* Like *Phèdre*, a tale that belabours the relationship between mind and body, The Wooster Group's production employs video production and technological installation to dramatize the cultural reproduction of the past. Directed by Elizabeth LeCompte, the play juxtaposes performer and pre-recorded performance to stimulate a sense of liveliness and disorienting insight. The stage is set for a game of Badminton, which the actors play with the ferocious energy underlining the battle between the two protagonists. The skilful use of digital mixed media interrogates the seamless capacities of technology to act as an unfiltered courier of perceptions of the past.

DJ SPOOKY

The Book of Ice, *2011.*
RIGHT *the artist in Antarctica.*
BELOW *poster for exhibition at the Plains Museum, Fargo, North Dakota.*

Experimental electronic musician, composer, author and artist, Paul Dennis Miller, known as DJ Spooky, is an 'intellectual DJ' who, since the early days of hip hop has used his turntables to scratch and remix works by avant-garde composers of late 20th-century music, from Iannis Xenakis and Ryuichi Sakamoto to jazz musicians Matthew Shipp and William Parker, Indie Rocker Thurston Moore and musician and pioneering visual artist Yoko Ono. He has also staged live remixings of D. W. Griffith's film *Birth of a Nation.* For *Arctic Rhythms,* Miller created a series of concerts of new compositions for turntable, violin and cello, using original sound recordings that he sourced during an expedition to the Antarctic.

CHRISTOPH SCHLINGENSIEF

LEFT Laying of the foundation stone for the African Opera Village, *2010.*
Ouagadougou.
Photo by Aino Laberebnz.
LEFT BELOW The Animatograph, *2005/2013.*
MoMA PS1, New York.
Photo by Matthew Septimus.

Director, filmmaker and provocateur Christoph Schlingensief's vision for an 'opera village' found form in Opendorf Afrika, an international centre for music, dance, film and opera that opened in 2009 in Ouagadougou, Burkina Faso, just two years before his untimely death. Designed with Francis Kéré, the village is now a twenty-three-structure complex that includes a performance space and school for adult education. The project exemplifies Schlingensief's foray into diverse forms of artistic engagement, and in many ways echoes the deeply felt concerns expressed in his films.

The Animatograph, a claustrophobic rotating carousel of technological and sculptural debris, is one of Schlingensief's many politically controversial projects. The enormous sculpture is covered in bizarre, crude images that include swastikas and projections of Hitler- and Stalin-themed porn. Viewers are invited to walk through the structure's dirty, winding interior – an Expressionist fever dream to be probed.

NELISIWE XABA

They Look at Me and That's All They Think, *2011.*
The Place, London.
Photo by Val Adamson.

Johannesburg-born Nelisiwe Xaba's performances are
one-act plays of ingenious costuming – eye-catching displays
that insist on the critical examination of identity, sexism and
exoticism with every move. As expressed unambiguously in the
title of this work, the very act of spectatorship layers the action
and its perception with long-held prejudices. Basing the piece
on the biography of Sarah Baartman, a South African Khoi
who became known as the 'Hottentot Venus' when exhibited in
London and France in the 1810s, Xaba devises wearable sculptural
constructions and shadow plays that show Baartman's story as
an allegory of her own artistic trajectory, exposing the clichés
of voyeurism through a singular visual theatre.

PAUL CHAN
Waiting for Godot, 2007.
New Orleans. Co-produced by Creative Time and
The Classical Theater of Harlem in New Orleans.
Photo by Frank Aymami.

This production of Beckett's *Waiting For Godot* in New Orleans
served as a means of reflecting on the conditions of the city post-Katrina.
Beckett's absurdist play was constructed in two outdoor locations that
had been significantly destroyed by the hurricane: a decimated street
in the Lower Ninth Ward and an abandoned house in the Gentilly
neighbourhood. Free to the public, the play began with a sermon from
the local Reverend, pre-show gumbo and a marching band that led the
audience to their seats. There was no finale, no grand crescendo. In a
post-Katrina landscape ravaged by innumerable disasters, Chan wanted
to use Beckett's bleak and empty play to make visible the absurdity and
beauty of hope in such a context. Neither Chan nor Beckett offers a
solution; Vladimir and Estragon never find Godot, and the audience is
left to contemplate their struggle of waiting. Chan did not produce his
piece in New Orleans to convey a 'message' or to reach a solution, but
to encourage reflection, and to provide support to its communities.

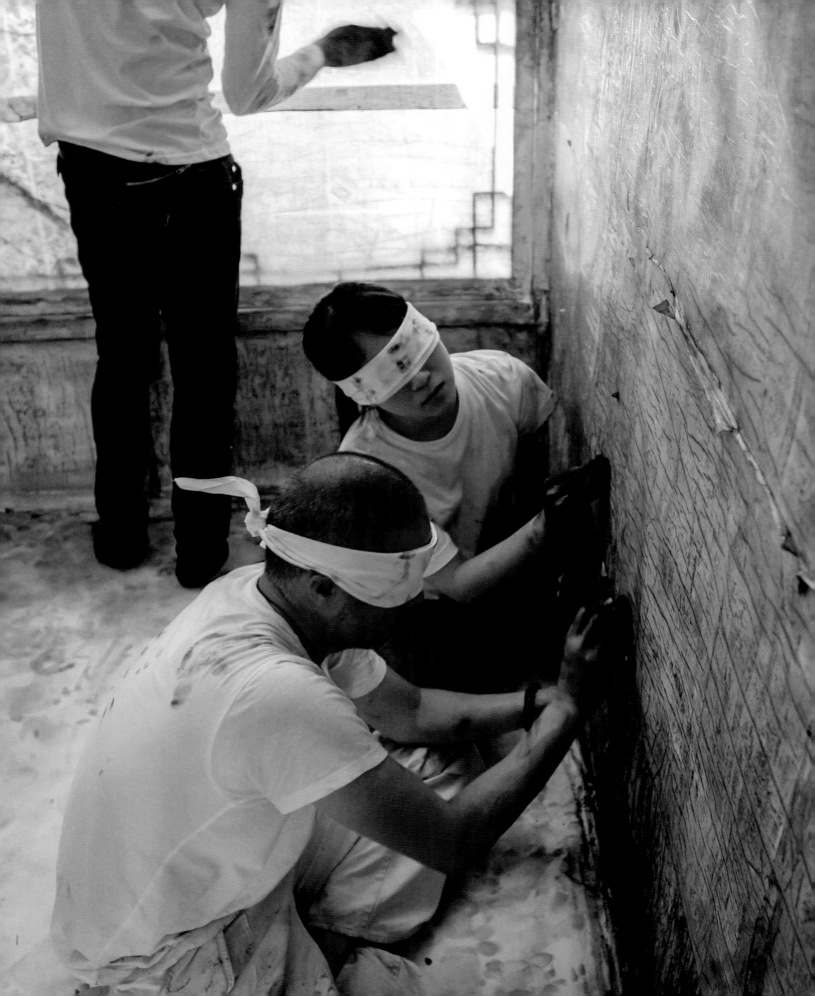

CHAPTER 6

Performing Architecture

Architecture has always been understood to involve a balance of theory and practice – of ideas and action, preparation and execution – the practice part of the equation traditionally referring to physical buildings. Yet for young architects coming into the profession in the early 1970s from depressed economies in the major capitals of Paris, London and New York, holding high the banners of radical intellectualism, deconstructivist critique of architectural history and social and political activism, the opportunity to apply their thinking to real construction was non-existent. Writing about architecture, teaching, exhibiting and giving presentations at conferences were significant options. Those who taught at the Architectural Association in London, the Institute for Urban Studies and Cooper Union in New York, or UP6 at the Beaux Arts in Paris, among them Rem Koolhaas, Diana Agrest, John Hejduk, Bernard Tschumi and the generation who followed them, including Nigel Coates, Zaha Hadid and Elizabeth Diller, begged off the idea of building altogether. Instead, each honed his or her critical and aesthetic manifestos, applying the deep research and investigative methodologies of their training to reinventing the idea of architecture as a powerful conceptual tool and activist platform. In doing so they established a dramatic reasoning that would inform their buildings at a later date.

DO HO SUH
Rubbing/Loving Project: Company Housing of Gwangju Theater, *2012. Commission for Gwangju Biennale.*

Not building was also in part a legacy of the radical architecture of 1960s utopianists and provocateurs including Cedric Price, Peter Cook and Ron Herron of Archigram, Super Studio and Archizoom, among many other groups who insisted that cultural criticism be as solid and foundational to contemporary architecture as any design debate. Social and political history, as well as points of view about technology and consumerism, freedom and control, lifestyle and economic reality, drove their parlance. The difference between a building and 'architecture' – between functional shell and futurist delirium – was debated in vibrant drawings, collages and texts in the large-format glossy magazines of the day (*Domus, Casabella, Architecture and Design*) that announced these visions to a small but expectant community on a regular basis. Similarly, conceptual artists of the 1970s used magazines as their exhibition space for work that investigated the underlying intellectual premises of art-making.

In contrast to these conceptually focused architects, visual artists had actual outlets for their creative visions: a gallery network and art spaces that exhibited their material with an immediacy and urgency that matched their deeply felt call for an art of ideas and stand against the art marketplace. They also had available to them the open-ended possibilities of live performance for realizing their ideas in space, in front of a small but growing audience of followers. In the storefront spaces of downtown New York, in artists' live-in lofts, on the streets, in parking lots, and on landfills along the Hudson River, visual artists were able to execute their cerebral propositions and to experiment on an ongoing basis, continuously expanding and developing the scope of their investigations while assembling new terminologies, techniques and materials. The evolving nature of this inventive work introduced new variables into film, video and photography, as well as into painting and sculpture. It seemed that mini-treatises, written or executed, about the body as material, the psychological quotient of space and the symbiotic relationship between performer and viewer were constantly being extended across different media. It made sense, then, that these concerns might also be something for architects to consider.

Such was the case with Elizabeth Diller and Ricardo Scofidio who, in the early 1980s when building commissions were scarce, chose to generate performances and installations in the avant-garde art and theatre worlds. Nine performances between 1983 and 1999, including *Civic Plots* and *Jet Lag,* allowed them to explore a number of recurrent obsessions:

how to increase the felt volumes of architecture; how to build structures that mediate the way viewers see them; how to 'stage' a building for visual effect. These performances served not only as life-sized working models for their ideas about architecture, but also provided a laboratory for the concepts that would eventually give their realized buildings their most distinctive qualities.

Diller and Scofidio's approach also served to underline the contrasting methodologies of artist and architect, beginning with how artists think and are trained versus the thinking and training of architects. Even though a single author might generate the first drawing and concept for a new architectural commission, the translation from initial gesture to realization is a long, involved and complex process. Research, preparation, drawing, blueprint and storyboard might take several if not many years to complete, each stage involving numerous people as well as technical and engineering know-how, critical contributions from many experts, attention to the expectations of the client and, of course, the assembly of significant financial resources. For artists, however, no such minutely considered proposals are expected – neither the months or years of accommodating a client, nor such a level of critical feedback and revision along the way. Licence to proceed with a work without permission to construct, after weighing of potentially significant architectural implications, and to execute a piece when and where the artist choses, is an enviable freedom. Architecturally scaled installations, having as much to do with works that inhabit or redraw the large volumes of a given space, such as those by Michael Beutler, Ann Hamilton, Laura Lima, Danh Vo or Ernesto Neto as well as such 1970s conceptual pioneers as Vito Acconci, Bruce Nauman, Dan Graham or Gordon Matta-Clark, offer propositions that can just as easily converse with architectural polemics.

For a new generation of architects, producing architectural interventions without the burdens of the profession is an irresistible enticement, and many are now venturing into the domain of the art gallery, museum or sculpture park. Drawn by the dramatic possibilities of temporary installation as well as by the appeal of engaging directly with audiences, and the increasing disposition of audiences towards event-driven cultural activities, a new field of highly visible architectural events – at architecture schools as well as at international architecture and design biennials – is taking shape. Architects, sometimes in collaboration with artists, choreographers or musicians, are expanding the nature and scope of this field,

ALEX SCHWEDER &
WARD SHELLEY
The Newcomers, 2017.
Commission for Performa 17,
Liberty Plaza, New York.
Photo by Paula Court.

providing ways to publicly demonstrate experiments that previously would have been confined to the specialized 'crit' of the graduate seminar classroom. How does sound invade the walls of a building? How is it possible to exhibit acoustics, showing the poetic sensibility that informs finished buildings, yet remains invisible to the naked eye? New outlets for such questions expand the relevance of architecture as a humanist discipline, making it accessible in entirely new ways to a public beyond the architectural community. For these performances and installations articulate architectural viewpoints and values in ways that drawings, axonometric projection and models cannot. They demonstrate, visually and viscerally, the nature of architectural learning: headings such as 'spatiotemporality', 'surface', 'time', 'place', 'material' – elements that are part of an essential inventory in the theory phase of architectural practice – can be activated and experienced in reality. Architecture as performance is now a working premise.

That many architects of the first decades of the 21st century are deeply engaged with contemporary art is in part a necessity, as the directors and boards of the contemporary art museums that are being constructed around the globe have come to comprise a new class of demanding and adventurous clients. Ever since the opening of the Guggenheim Bilbao by Frank Gehry in 1997, and Tate Modern – Herzog & de Meuron's remake of a Bankside Power Station – in London in 2000, it is these kinds of 'museums of the future', which anticipate multimedia exhibitions for high-capacity audiences, that architects are being asked to imagine and design. Conversations with curators and artists, and now performers and choreographers, are essential to the process of these architects. Museums as containers for a broad range of cultural activities,

a series of voluble performance spaces in themselves, are being designed with spectacular halls where hundreds may gather, and multi-storeyed artworks are routinely commissioned to fill them. Tech requirements for lighting systems, sprung floors, purpose-built greenrooms and recording, editing and conservation facilities, as well as flexible spaces for dance, music and live performance are changing the look and the function of these buildings. Some have themselves been designed to be in motion, as in Rem Koolhaas' super-flexible renovation of a 19th-century building in Le Marais in Paris for the Lafayette Foundation. A central gallery space on elevator tracks at its core moves up or down to expand or reduce spaces on different levels according to artists' specifications, and their desire for intimate or expansive spaces. Koolhaas conceived the building as an always-changing theatre for art – an intimate place of focus and experimentation that in its variability provides a systematic way to escape architectural stagnation.

Buildings that move, and in so doing question domestic or social landscapes, acting as metaphors for balance and compatibility, routine and unpredictability, are in the ever-expanding domain of Alex Schweder. His re-conceptualization of architecture emphasizes the everyday actions naturally scripted into buildings, and the built environment that we inhabit. 'Performance architecture', as he names the unorthodox temporary structures in which he lives for up to ten days at a time with fellow artist Ward Shelley, provides a way for him to examine the complexity of architectural arguments, and to do so up-close and in conversation with viewers. Outfitted to be lived in, each with a toilet and kitchen as well as sleep and work stations, the unexpected shapes of these constructions – a half-a-metre-wide (2 ft), four-

DILLER SCOFIDIO + RENFRO
Blur *(braincoat), 2002.*
Photograph of project design.
Commission for Expo.02, Lake Neuchâtel,
Switzerland.

storey edifice, an elevated house balanced on a single point that spins in the wind and tilts with the shifting weight of those inside – demand that each person find new behaviours in the process of occupation.

Performance also provides a critical tool for examining the controversies of architecture; to articulate fierce disagreements with relentlessly commercial developments that blatantly ignore the mixed communities around them. Aggressive, expensive, and representing power and might, the towers that high capitalism affords continue to be built regardless of the social and economic distress, homelessness, and the numbers of displaced migrants that mount daily in cities large and small. Some architects question the role of their discipline in acceding to the demands of the 'one per cent', and issue proposals for common spaces and the comfort of community as counterpoints to these harsh divisions. With names such as 'Office for Political Innovation (OPI)' (Andre Jaque's office in Madrid and New York), 'Laboratoire de Architecture, Performance et Sabotage' (Didier Faustino's practice in Paris and Berlin) and 'Office for Subversive Architecture' (OSA) (a collective network of architects with members in London, Berlin, Vienna and Darmstadt) these activist studios make public their approaches to the hierarchies of architecture through live performance, installations and built structures. OPI, which includes an economist, a sociologist and a journalist on the team, explores the implications of today's socially indifferent property developments through interactive buildings and the use of various media in installations and houses that are as colourful as they are highly designed platforms for public participation. Faustino invites viewers to fit themselves into his built forms, enacting the shape of Yves Klein's *Leap into the Void* (*Opus Incertum*, 2008), or climbing a staircase to nowhere (*Stairway to Heaven*, 2001), in works that examine the political and ethical underpinnings of public sites while also reflecting on the relationship of the body to buildings. OSA, by contrast, inserts itself into already existing public spaces to fashion intimate hubs for social engagement (as in *Hoegaarden*, 2005, a grass-covered outdoor pub built into a sidewalk) or to point to the wastefulness of long-standing buildings that seem to have been randomly abandoned or slated for demolition (as in *Accumulator*, 2008, a giant funnel directing rain water into a defunct swimming pool).

Commitment to an architectural process that can straddle politics, economics and crisis management, treating issues related to health and housing, immigration and community, forms the basis of the Teddy Cruz Studio situated at the border of the United States and Mexico, at the point where the material excesses of San Diego's urban sprawl spill over into the under-served shantytowns of Tijuana. Observing how discarded objects – from traffic cones to car tyres, truck beds, garage doors and prefabricated houses – are recycled from north to south, using the waste of San Diego to create viable structures in the slums of Tijuana, Cruz and his team, 'Cross Border Initiative' (at the University of California in San Diego), including political scientist Fonna Forman, use the creative intelligence that comes of necessity to those living at the border as the foundation for an architecture of inclusion. For Cross Border Initiative, the wall between Mexico and the United States is a site for problem-solving rather than one of policing and instability. Their 'unwalling' activities, as they describe their architectural activism, realized in housing complexes on both sides of the divide, allow people to see each other beyond fences and to participate in the social and economic reorganization necessary for more equitable cities.

Such reimaginings of an architecture 'on the move' arise amid the urgency for instant solutions to alleviate the despair of millions of immigrants and refugees fleeing war zones in many parts of the world. These issues are a high-alert trigger for architects to find design solutions for 'temporary' settlements that are in fact anything but temporary, and that can provide a place of safety and refuge – even the capacity to rekindle fragments of community. In Berlin as in Frankfurt, Jordan and Turkey, architects must consider emergency humanitarian design – 'instant cities' that recognize mobile communities and imagine new architectural and urban structures to accommodate them. They and the municipalities they serve must also consider the necessary conditions for re-inhabiting towns and villages in the countryside, in France as well as England and Germany, from which vast numbers have moved to urban centres, calling for the repopulation of such denuded places by those without home or country.

Mobility between vastly different cultures has allowed Diébédo Francis Kéré, born in the rural village of Gando, Burkina Faso, and trained as an architect in Berlin, to apply the training methods of one to the long-held traditional building methods of the other. This practice of combination has as much to do with the communal belief system instilled in Kéré as a child in a West African settlement as to inventing a new architecture to suit its climate and economy. In the semi-arid savannah with its oppressive heat, brought by hot and dry Saharan winds, interrupted by a monsoon season with frequent flooding, Kéré built the first primary school in Gando in 2004 as part of his graduating diploma. Together with the men and women of Gando, using local building methods and materials, Kéré constructed a natural air cooling and water preservation system that created a model for ecological and sustainable architecture. Commissioned to design a temporary theatre for Berlin's famous Volksbühne Theater in one of the monumental aeroplane hangars at the old Tempelhof Airport, where more than 8,000 refugees are currently housed, Kéré once again brings his participatory ethos of inclusivity and communal celebration to drive his design: Volksbühne Tempelhof will respond to the many traditions, cultures and languages of those living in housing units on site. A structure that itself 'performs' inside and outside the hangar with its extraordinary ceiling height and massive roller doors, this universal mobile stage will demand radical experimentation from its performers, directors, media technicians and stagehands alike.

Architecture as performance, visceral and experiential, is an overt teaching tool for architects in training as well as for audiences. It underlines the profound implications of architecture, for every building carries within it social and economic realms that seep into their surroundings, even as the structure itself goes some way towards establishing an objective monumental hierarchy. Fraught with their antithesis, permanence, the ephemeral gestures of performance insist on an imaginary architecture as a place of enquiry (intellectual, aesthetic, political), while the poetics of performance space adds a real and relatable vocabulary to the discipline, infinitely expanding the idea of architecture and the kinds of mental, emotional and actual spaces that we can inhabit. Whether they be works of procession by artists or architects such as Arto Lindsay, Francis Alÿs or Bryony Roberts, dance as 'liquid architecture' by choreographers such as Anne Teresa De Keersmaeker, Yve Laris Cohen or Gerard & Kelly, or sound installations by Bernard Leitner, Katarzyna Krakowiak or Marina Rosenfeld, the discourse of architecture is exponentially expanded through actions. Space and surface, time and place, data and materials are each reconfigured and reconsidered in entirely new ways through the matrix of the 'live', infinitely enhancing our experience, as well as our knowledge and understanding, of the spaces that we occupy.

RAUMLABOR
Monuments, *2013.*
City square, Nantes.

Developed in three phases, *Monuments*, the work of
experimental architectural collaborative Raumlabor, explores
the 'creation of a moment', celebrating public urban space
as a setting for unplanned occasions. Phase one involved the
conceptualization and construction of objects in an open
dialogue over dinners and workshops at an 'art production camp'
in the courtyard of the École des Beaux-Arts in Nantes. Phase
two saw the built structures moved into the city 'surprising the
public' in the manner of a Trojan horse, and phase three was
the memory of the intervention – as embedded experience, as
exhibition and as debris from the deconstructed objects. The
six imposing structures – including a smoke-emitting plinth, an
obelisk and a cylinder launching a whirlwind of paper strips –
were moved through Nantes, interrupting the static public space
and celebrating the potential for curious interactions within it.

THOMAS HIRSCHHORN

RIGHT Bataille Monument, *2001.*
Commission for Documenta 11, Kassel.
Photo by Werner Maschmann.
CENTRE Gramsci Monument, *2013.*
Forst House, Bronx, New York.
Photo by Romain Lopez.
BELOW Deleuze Monument, *2000.*
La Beauté, Avignon.

Thomas Hirschhorn uses a vast collection of found objects to create sprawling installations, collages and interactive environments that reflect the wastefulness of our consumerist society while providing a space for public gathering. In this series, he constructed four temporary monuments dedicated to iconic philosophers: Spinoza, Deleuze, Bataille and Gramsci. Hirschhorn recruited local residents to help build these infrastructures with materials including plywood, aluminium sheets, plastic wrap and brown packing tape. Located primarily in working-class neighbourhoods, the interconnected rooms, walkways, books, newspapers and sculptures became makeshift playgrounds, offering public programming, jobs and an information hub for the community.

ANN HAMILTON

the event of a thread, *2012.*
Commission from Park Avenue Armory.
Photo by Ian Douglas.

Hamilton uses sound and a broad array of materials, from straw to dough, to brass pennies and honey in her large-scale, poetic installations. This oversized playground in Park Avenue Armory's vast Drill Hall featured more than forty giant swings and a billowing white curtain. Reaching across the hall's 36.5-metre (120 ft) width, and attached to pulleys connected to swings dangling from supports 21 metres (70 ft) above the ground, the curtain swings dramatically with each back and forth motion of the swingers. Also in the space, providing a spoken word soundtrack for these exhilarating movements, a lone figure jots notes while two people sit facing stacks of caged pigeons, reading aloud philosophical and literary texts from large scrolls.

YVE LARIS COHEN
Fine, *2015.*
The Kitchen, New York.
Photo by Paula Court.

Yve Laris Cohen, who applies his training in classical
ballet to installation work, drew from the failed execution
of an unrealized piece to create *Fine*, a black-box performance.
Al Fine, the intended performance and installation, is
presented in terms of its complications and eventual
abandonment, detailed by the artist through oral history
and memory. Crammed against a shifting black curtain,
the audience listened to dialogues – some live and some as
audio recordings – from technicians and engineers as well
as figures from the artist's youth. The piece and its processes
are eulogized by Laris Cohen, marking the limitations of
creation and realization.

MICHAEL BEUTLER
Yellow Escalator, *2006.*
Commission for Berlin Biennial, Post Office Stables.
Photo by the artist.

Repurposing industrial material for his large-scale installations, Michael Beutler builds sculptural structures that respond directly to their exhibition space. In a former post office in Berlin, Beutler created *Yellow Escalator*, an imposing, electric-yellow staircase supported by rows of thin, towering beams. The construction of the steps is fully exposed, the staircase branching out into two smaller paths before ending abruptly mid-air, never reaching an upper level. Although built with industrial Pecafil, the steps can neither be walked on nor ridden, the architectural object only hinting at an escalator's function while displaying its form.

MARCO FUSINATO
Aetheric Plexus (Broken X), *2013.*
National Gallery of Victoria, Melbourne.

Using technical equipment associated with staged spectacles, from bright spotlights to powerful surround speakers, Melbourne-based Fusinato's multi-sensorial installations spring into action when triggered by viewers getting too close. Rows of lighting, wiring and speakers held together on a scaffold of white tubing first appear as dormant towering sculptures but, when approached, blast overwhelming noise and blinding light at the unsuspecting participants. Combining a sparse conceptual aesthetic with 'noise music', the artist creates spaces that are psychologically dense with the sounds and violence of an imposing authority.

DILLER SCOFIDIO + RENFRO
Blur, *2002.*
Commission for Expo.02, Lake Neuchâtel, Switzerland.

DS + R have been celebrated since the early 1980s for
finding ways to make architecture even without leaving
any trace of an actual building. This ultimate ephemeral
building was made of artificial cloud, billowing 20 metres
(65 ft) high over Lake Neuchâtel in Switzerland. Elegantly
streamlined bridges led viewers across the water towards a
ghostly pavilion, shrouded in a mist produced by 35,000 fog
nozzles, generating a visual and auditory white-out. Visitors
wore transparent 'braincoats' (smart raincoats) to explore the
infinity of the watery walls around them, each embedded with
computer chips carrying information about the character
and profile of the wearer (provided in a questionnaire before
entering). The system allowed for communication both
with the cloud's computer network and between visitors,
establishing the Blur as the first interative AI building.

LUCY + JORGE ORTA

Modular Architecture – The Unit x 10, *1996/2003.*
Fondation Cartier, Paris.
Photo by John Akehurst.

Constructing survivalist, tent-like shelters and
communal sculptures, the Ortas merge site-specific activism
with a futuristic, environmentally-conscious aesthetic. Their
first piece of choreography, *Modular Architecture*, placed twelve
dancers in utilitarian, wearable equipment – a cross between
a bivouac and a sci-fi sleeping bag. The dancers assemble
in geometric variations on the floor, joining in pairs and
combining their forms. Beside them stands a silver dome,
gloves and arms dangling from its surface. In the later series
Nexus Architecture, the artists explore notions of community
and human bonds through radical public formations.
Attached by umbilical overalls, performers symbolically and
physically merge to form an interconnected, living sculpture.

DO HO SUH
Rubbing/Loving Project: Company Housing of
Gwangju Theater, *2012.*
Commission for Gwangju Biennale.

Since the 1990s, Do Ho Suh has been building full-scale, gem-hued
textile replications of buildings or apartments that hold particular
personal meaning for him. He has also made several 'rubbings' of a
range of these venues that he captures in great detail on thin sheets
of vellum pasted over entire surfaces – floors, ceilings, door handles,
kitchen appliances. These are gently rubbed with coloured pastels
and, once completed, carefully peeled off the surfaces and reinstalled
on purpose-built supports, amassing an expansive catalogue of place.
Rubbing/Loving is a tribute to the New York apartment and studio
where he lived and worked for almost two decades. In a process that
took three years, his overall drawing captured each dent and scratch
of daily living, memorializing the space and its history in ghostly detail.

SOPHIE CALLE
Room, *2011.*
Lowell Hotel, New York.

Thirty years after *The Hotel*, 1981 – a series of photographs made during a three-week stint as a chambermaid in a Venice hotel of twelve guests' rooms and their belongings – Calle returned to hotel territory, this time featuring her own belongings in the Lowell, New York. Two wedding dresses (one white, one red), a wig, a framed portrait of Freud and a stuffed cat, brought from home in Paris, were strewn across the room and interspersed with local items such as a burnt mattress and a baby stroller. Each object has its own notecard-caption, and the artist appears occasionally over the course of a long weekend, sometimes conversing with late-night viewers. This staged installation-memoir is, according to the artist, a long-term project with no end, and evokes the many narratives contained within hotel architecture.

GERARD & KELLY
Modern Living, *2016.*
The Glass House, New Canaan, Connecticut.

Choreographers Gerard & Kelly are known for their
use of video, choreography and installation to approach
the dynamics of coupling and queer intimacy. *Modern Living*
was a dual bi-coastal performance at the Glass House in
Connecticut and the Schindler House in California. Working
with nine dancers from the L.A. Dance Project in modernist
homes with striking natural landscapes, performers in various
configurations waded in a pool, posed in a garden, or sat
across from each other at a dinner table, each moving tableau
interpreting the given domestic arrangements within the
house. Whether solo, in pairs or as an ensemble, the dancers
explored the emotional states of home: isolation, interaction,
transparency and voyeurism, the separate scenes creating
further dialogue between the two edifices.

GELITIN
Tantamounter 24/7, 2005.
Commission for Performa 05, New York.
Photos by Paula Court.

Four-man Viennese collective Gelitin
emphasize the experience of play, child-like
spontaneity and humour verging on absurdity in
their performances and interactive projects. This
room-size 'duplication machine' saw the group
housed for seven days inside a makeshift plywood
contraption that they had filled with building
supplies – cardboard, fabric, paint and stitching
devices – which they would use to make life-sized
replicas of personal objects that viewers were
invited to submit through a large hatch in the
outer wall. Inside, the group worked quickly to
make copies of each object – a camera, a Chinese
cup, even a young child (a friend of the artists),
who was game to enter the large box. After some
time, the copy would be sent back out the hatch
to its waiting owner.

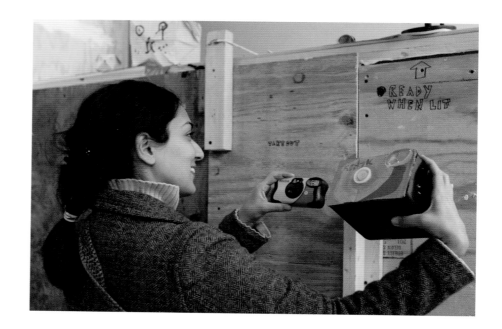

JONAH FREEMAN & JUSTIN LOWE
Stray Light Grey, *2012.*
Marlborough Gallery, New York.
Photo by Todd Eberle.

Known for constructing sprawling, dystopian installations of meth labs and themed cityscapes, for *Stray Light Grey* Freeman and Lowe transformed a white-walled gallery into a disturbing, psychedelic urban environment. Named for cyberpunk author William Gibson's *Villa Stray Light* from his *Sprawl* trilogy, and drawing on the artists' earlier imaginary worlds such as the San San International – a youth-culture-driven sprawling metropolis between San Diego and San Juan, the installation becomes progressively more surreal as viewers walk through grime-stained corridors and haphazardly blasted dry-walls. A futuristic plastic-surgeon's office, some components of which came from a defunct veterinary office, or a library full of renamed books, the rooms are structurally familiar yet eerily subverted – an unsettling parallel world to our own.

ARTO LINDSAY
Somewhere I Read, 2009.
Commission for Performa 09, Times Square, New York.
Photo by Paula Court.

Arto Lindsay has been experimenting with instrumental
techniques and avant-garde sound since the 1970s, and
choreographed this mesmerizing parade in Times Square for
Performa 09. Fifty dancers wearing identical beige coats move
in synchrony, cued by a pre-recorded electronic score that each
performer listens to on a flip-phone held to one ear. Amid the
cacophony of brightly lit billboards, the crush of passers-by
and the mid-town traffic, this unusual parade manages to
focus the crowd, which enthusiastically swells in number as
it follows the performers for several blocks down Broadway.

DIDIER FAUSTINO
Opus Incertum, *2008.*
Centre national des arts plastiques, Paris.

French architect Faustino established 'sabotage' as a defining concept in his approach to architecture, even founding an agency called LAPS (Laboratoire d'Architecture, Performance et Sabotage) on graduating from architecture school. His actions often force the viewer into strange positions, as with *Opus Incertum* (Uncertain Work), a sculptural object of painted wood that is moulded to fit a body, face down, so as to induce the experience of Yves Klein's *Leap into the Void.* The piece indirectly reflects on such considerations as verticality, and the symbiotic nature of human body and architectural form. A handwritten sign on the wall 'You are invited to try me out' makes the expected viewer participation completely clear.

RENATA LUCAS
Kunst-Werke, *2010.*
Kunst-Werke Institute for Contemporary Art, Berlin.
Photo by Uwe Walter.

Brazilian artist Renata Lucas's playful, spatially warped installations shift the viewer's perception of space and place. In this piece, a large circle is cut into a gallery floor. Half concrete, half grass, the room can be viewed empty or with a half-moon carpet, by pushing on a moveable wall. Outside the gallery, a slab of sidewalk has been tilted 7.5 degrees counter-clockwise, leaving stones jutting into the street. In both sculptures, Lucas manipulates Kunst-Werke's pre-existing topographies, disrupting their expected forms.

STUDIO MIESSEN
Performa 09 Hub, *2009.*
Cooper Union, New York.
Photos by Paula Court.

This expansive, versatile plywood wall functioned as a seamless, multi-use hub for Performa 09. Wrapped around three sides of Cooper Union's ground floor, the structure condensed the organizational, practical and performance needs of the Performa Biennial into a singular infrastructure. The space was able to act as an office, bookshop, lounge, performance and screening area and a small, tiered amphitheatre. A series of moveable doors, alcoves and panels allowed the temporary architecture multiple orientations, creating a streamlined form adaptable to its myriad functions.

ERNESTO NETO
anthropodino, 2009.
Commission from Park Avenue Armory for
Wade Thompson Drill Hall, New York.
Photo by Jean Vong.

Using the elastic qualities of diaphanous Lycra to
create immersive, biomorphic installations, Ernesto Neto
transformed the vast hangar-like structure of the Park
Avenue Armory's drill hall, with its wooden floors and
gigantic latticework steel truss, into a pastel labyrinth of
soft-sculpture tunnels, woven beneath an elaborately draped
canopy. With its textured, transparent caverns, skeletal rods
and dangling spice-filled cocoons, the space invites viewers
to interact actively with the amorphous, suspended forms –
the environment both corporeal and extra-terrestrial.

SNARKITECTURE
Dig, 2011.
Storefront for Art and Architecture, New York.

Visual artist Daniel Arsham and architect Alex Mustonen combine their training in visual art and architecture respectively in suggestive, experience-driven projects. Their works for public spaces, retail shops and the stage frequently play with existing structures to create literal pathways for performer and audience, suggesting the ongoing malleability of architecture. *Dig* was both exhibition and explication. Staged in three parts – exhibition, installation and performance – each part indicates where its ideas came from and where they are going next. The storefront itself is packed to the brim with industrial foam with diagrams plotting the artists' intentions. Arsham tunnels through the foam armed with hammers and picks, showing the evolution of the project from concept to construction and demolition, all as part of a whole.

OSA/KHBT
Urban Oasis, 2005.
Museo de Arte de Zapopan.
Photo by Johannes Marburg.

Karsten Huneck and Bernd Trümpler (KHBT) are partners in the Office for Subversive Architecture, an open community of architects, artists and designers, the members of which live and work in cities across Europe including Berlin, Darmstadt, Frankfurt, Graz, London, Vienna and Munich. Creating both minimal, temporary installations and permanent buildings, they transform existing structures and public spaces, manipulating and adding to them to encourage, in their words, a 'pause' in urban life. *Hoegaarden*, an outdoor, specially built grass-covered pub, was open to the public for one week. Signs read 'Keep on the grass'.

LOS CARPINTEROS
Show Room, *2017*.
Lisbon.
Photo by Daniel Martin Corona.

Los Carpinteros create meticulous sculptures, drawings and large-scale installations that engage the political dynamics underlying urban infrastructures. In *Show Room*, the Havana-based collective reconstruct the explosion of a brick wall. With concrete chunks flying in all directions, the fragments are frozen in their violent trajectory, suspended in the air by dozens of thin wires. Static and observable, the moment of destruction appears both delicate and dangerous, its form simultaneously extracted from and dependent on the violence that produced it and resulting in an unnerving installation for the gallery visitor.

TOBIAS PUTRIH
Design studio for MUDAM, *2006.*
Musée d'Art Moderne Grand-Duc Jean, Luxembourg.
Photo by Rémi Villaggi.

Using basic materials to build modular sculptures, Putrih created this sculptural environment-as-studio for education and public workshops within the MUDAM Museum. Each plywood section can be taken apart, put together and rearranged, resembling both scientific diagrams and interactive building blocks. The structures propose a physical dialogue between art and audience, encouraging interaction while demonstrating the relationship between creation, function and reception.

BRYONY ROBERTS

We Know How to Order, *2015*
*Commission for Chicago Architecture
Biennial, Federal Art Center, Chicago.
Photos by Andrew Bruah.*

Creating dynamic, site-specific
installations and performances that interrupt
pre-existing architectures with a disruptive,
commanding human presence, Bryony
Roberts collaborated with Chicago's South
Shore Drill Team on *We Know How To Order*
(2015), a public intervention that disrupted
a modernist space, merging marching band
routines with fluid street choreography.
Transforming the imposing Mies van der
Rohe's Federal Center, the teenage drill
group performed an expressive, mesmerizing
choreography – their grid-like precision
echoing modernist sensibilities as their white
drill flags billowed in the air. The precise,
visually captivating movements commanded
the plaza, questioning the political barriers
of occupying a public architecture, whom
they were built for, and what it means for a
South Side youth organization to demand
space within them.

ANDRÉS JAQUE
IKEA Disobedients, *2011.*
Madrid.

IKEA Disobedients was a makeshift domestic environment modelled after nine individuals' non-traditional uses of interior space. Amid stacked and purposefully mis-assembled IKEA furnishings, these individuals were invited to perform their alternative household routines. Including a living-room beauty salon and an improvised aquaphonics lab, the environments resisted the sterile, traditional images of home life proposed by furniture manufacturers and their advertisers. During two performances visitors explore the room, as the performers reveal an architectural rendering of sociopolitical dynamics.

LAURA LIMA
Gala Chickens, *2015*.
Commission for Performa 15, 350 Broadway, New York.
Photo by Paula Court.

Brazilian artist Laura Lima stages performances that actively transform space while also physically confining and directing viewers. In response to Performa's investigation of performance by artists during the Italian Renaissance, Lima built a full-sized chicken coop to house a collection of ornamental chickens adorned with carnival feathers. The piece, which took place over several days, culminated in an event that involved viewers selecting from sixty Renaissance costumes that they wore over their clothes. Impromptu participants become central actors and instigators within the surprising architecture of a house for chickens transformed by the elegance of 15th-century fashion. The work points to the myriad possibilities of collective formation and action.

ALEX SCHWEDER & WARD SHELLEY
ReActor House, 2016.
Omi International Arts Center, Ghent.
Photo by Richard Barnes.

Architect Alex Schweder and visual artist Ward Shelley use their bodies as tools of balance in their precisely-designed architectural structures. *ReActor* is a precarious home that balances on a 4.5-metre (15 ft) concrete pillar, allowing the house to rotate 360 degrees and tilt depending on the whereabouts of the two inhabitants. Their first piece outdoors, the structure invites the changing weather, of wind or rain, to determine the motion of the elevated house. Wearing red and orange jumpsuits, Schweder and Shelley co-exist in the home's symmetrical, glass-walled interiors for five days, altering the building's orientation and mobility with each movement of their daily routine.

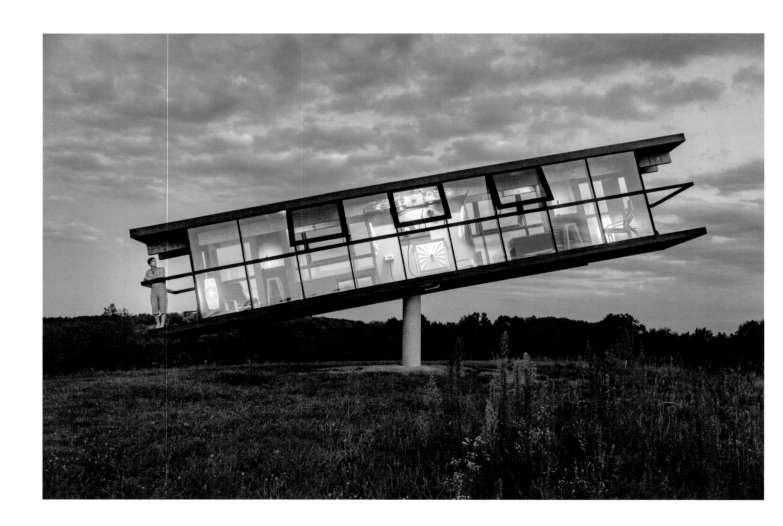

MIKE NELSON

LEFT Quiver of Arrows, *2010.*
303 Gallery, New York.
BELOW 408 Tonnes of Imperfect Geometry, *2012.*
Malmö Konsthall.

Known for constructing labyrinthine, disorienting and psychologically infused environments – derelict trailers, rooms of sand, assemblages of cultural debris, quasi stage sets – that conjure architectures of the mind as much as visceral, walkthrough experiences, in *408 Tonnes of Imperfect Geometry* Nelson stretches the architectural conceit of a building in Malmö, Sweden, by setting individually cast pieces of concrete across the wooden floor, deliberately confronting the load-bearing capacity of the infrastructure. Adjacent to the sculptural latticework (a motif borrowed from traditional Muslim ornamentation) and separated by a glass wall, viewers can observe the production workshop itself – its tools, concrete moulds and pouring processes. They are thus given access to the elegant and precarious balance of design, material, engineering, emotion and movement – all persistent elements of architecture.

PICTURE CREDITS

Walid Raad. Courtesy Paula Cooper Gallery, New York. **120b** Photo by Walid Raad. © Walid Raad. Courtesy Paula Cooper Gallery. **121** Anri Sala © DACS 2018. **122–123** Courtesy the artist and Rossi & Rossi. **124** Courtesy the artist. **125** Courtesy the artist. **127** © Olaf Pascheit. Courtesy the artist and Sfeir-Semler Galloery Beirut/Hamburg. **128–129** © Emily Jacir. Courtesy Alexander and Bonin, New York. **130** Courtesy the artist and Giorgio Persano Gallery. Courtesy David Zwirner, New York/London. **134** Courtesy the artist, Walied Osman and the Farouk Foundation. **135** Courtesy of the artist, Clifton Benevito, New York and Isabella Bortolozzi, Berlin. **136** Courtesy Debus Sinyakov. **139** Courtesy Annet Gelink Gallery Amsterdam. **140** Courtesy the artists. **141** Courtesy Shady Lane Productions, Berlin and Tanya Bonakdar Gallery, New York. **142** Photo by Naho Kubota. Courtesy Mor Charpentier Galerie; PPOW Galerie, New York. **143** © 2017 Legendary. **144** Courtesy Ronald Feldman Gallery, New York. **146** © Martin Creed. Courtesy the artist and Hauser & Wirth. **147** Photo © Paula Court. © Rashaad Newsome Studio. **148** Photography Ken Adard. © Ai Weiwei. Courtesy Lisson Gallery. **149** Photo Victor Perez. Courtesy prometeogallery di Ida Pisani, Milano/Lucca. **150** Photo Teresa Margolles. Courtesy the artist and Galerie Peter Kilchmann, Zurich. **151** Courtesy the artist. **155** Santiago Sierra © DACS 2018. **158** Photo by Dominik Mentzos. **161** Courtesy the artist. **163** Photo Miana Jun. **164** Photo by Hugo Glendinning. **165** © Yi-Chun (2010). **168** Courtesy the artist. **170** © Paula Court. **172** Photo by Paula Court, Courtesy the Kitchen and David Kordansky Gallery. **173** Photo by Elizabeth Proitsis. Courtesy Performa. **174** Courtesy Studio Anne Imhof and Galerie Bortolozzi. **175** Photo Herman Sugeloos. **176** © Dieter Schwer. **179** Courtesy the artist. **180** © Peter Hönneman. **181** Produced by LISA and I'M'COMPANY, in co-production with Sophiensaele Berlin (DE), Productiehuis Rotterdam/Rotterdamse Schouwburg (NL), Dubbelspel (30CC and STUK Kuntstencentrum Leuven, BE). © L. Bernaerts, I. Müller and Driest Ontwerpen. **182** Photo by Yi-Chun Wu. **183** Photo by Ian Douglas. Courtesy the artist and TBSP MGMT. **184** Photo Bryan Thatcher. © Sens Productions 2006. **185** Photo Manuel Vason. **186** Photos by Elise Fitte-Duval and Gennadi Nash. Courtesy Nora Chipaumire. **188** © Agathe Poupeney. Courtesy Faustin Linyekula. **189** Photo by Charles Roussel. **190** Courtesy the artist; Frith Street Gallery, London and Marian Goodman Gallery, New York/Paris. **191** © Sharon Lockhart. Courtesy the artist; Gladstone Gallery, New York and Brussels; Neugerriemschneider, Berlin. **192** © Laurent Philippe. **193** Photo by Alain Monot. **194** Photo by Julieta Cervantes. © 2015 The Museum of Modern Art, New York. **199** Courtesy Elevator Repair Service. **200** Photo © Paula Court. **205** Photo Teddy Wolff. **206** Lisa Whiteman. **207** © Big Art Group. **211** RW Work, Ltd. **212** Photo courtesy the artists. **215** Courtesy the artist. **216a** Courtesy My Barbarian/ Susanne Vielmetter Los Angeles Projects. **217** Courtesy the artist and Metro Pictures, New York. **223** Courtesy the artists. **226** Courtesy the artist. **227** Courtesy the artist. **228** Courtesy the artists. **229a** Courtesy the artist and Galerie Micheline Szwajcer. **233a** Photo Matthew Septimus. © 2014 MoMA PS1. **233b** Photo Aino Laberenz. **235** Photo Frank Amami. Courtesy Creative Time. **236** © Do Ho Suh. Courtesy the artist and Lehmann Maupin, New York and Hong Kong. **240** Courtesy Diller, Scofidio and Renfro. **242** © Machine Machine. **243a** Courtesy Gladstone Gallery, New York and Brussels. **243b** Courtesy Dia Art Foundation. **243c** Courtesy DRAC Provence-Alpes-Côte d'Azur, Aix-en-Provence. **244** Photo by Ian Douglas. **246a** Photo by Michael Beutler. Courtesy Galerie Bärbel Grässlin. **246b** Courtesy of the artist and Anna Schwartz Gallery. **247** Courtesy Diller, Scofido and Renfro. **248** Photographer John Akehurst. Courtesy Lucy and Jorge Orta. **249** © Do Ho Suh. Courtesy the artist Lehmann Maupin, New York and Hong Kong. **250** © Sophie Calle/ADGAP, Paris and ARS, New York, 2017. **251** Courtesy the artists **253** © Todd Eberle. Courtesy Marlborough Contemporary, New York and London. **255** Photo by Uwe Walter. Courtesy the artist. **257** Courtesy the artist and Yanya Bonakdar Gallery, New York. **259** Photo Daniel Martin Cornona. © Los Carpinteros. **260** © Remi Villaggi. **261** Courtesy the artist. **262** © André Jaque. **265a** © Mike Nelson. Courtesy 303 Gallery, New York. **265b** Courtesy Malmö Konsthall.

INDEX

ACKNOWLEDGMENTS

First and foremost, my infinite gratitude to Marc Arthur, who has been in turn my research assistant, teaching assistant, colleague, collaborator and friend, as we have worked together building a contemporary performance archive of work by artists in a range of mediums from around the world, which is the core material of this book. He has helped me, together with Quinn Schoen, to compile almost three hundred captions that introduce the reader to each image. He, along with the Performa team (especially Esa Nickle, Job Piston, Adrienne Edwards, Charles Aubin, Defne Ayas and Mark Beaseley) is a vigilant witness to and constant resource for contemporary art and performance as it is being created in New York and elsewhere. Marc has developed a digital reference system that houses texts, interviews, images, essays, video and audio on a scale that makes retrieval a fascinating process in and of itself. With such archiving comes knowledge and discernment, and it is for all of this that I thank Marc, as well as for his warmth and good company.

Thanks to the artists presented in this book, for their extraordinary insights and imagination, for their talents, abilities and courage, for they reveal to us the worlds in which we live, and do so in deeply moving and remarkable ways. To the photographers, foremost among them Paula Court, who capture history as it is being made, each providing a particular point of view. To the team at Thames & Hudson led by Roger Thorp, including Amber Husain and Anna Perotti, and Thomas Neurath, publisher of my first and several subsequent books, my deepest gratitude. My heartfelt thanks always to my husband, Dakota Jackson, and grown children Zoe Jackson and Pierce Jackson and their growing families for their constant inspiration.

This book describes an ongoing living history of work being produced around the globe. It can only be a partial history of performance since 2000, and a stepping stone to many more. Even as I sign off on this edition, I salute in anticipation the new work of artists to come.